Life and Values

Edited by Edwin and Helen Alderfer

Mennonite Publishing House
Scottdale, Pennsylvania

Meditation

Holding a beggar's child
Against my heart,
Through blinding tears I see
That as I love the tiny, piteous thing,
So God loves me!
Toyohiko Kagawa

(Lois J. Erickson — int.)

LIFE AND VALUES
Copyright © 1974 by Mennonite Publishing House, Scottdale, Pa. 15683
Printed in USA.

Contents

Preface

"Lord, let me know my end,
and what is the measure of my days;
let me know how fleeting my life is!"
   — Psalm 39:4

This study guide is a working tool for people who are ready to seriously consider the questions on life and values that are being raised in our culture. Questions such as:

1. What resources would you have to offer to someone faced with an unwanted pregnancy?

2. Should the church engage in the study of abortion, euthanasia, test-tube fertilization, fetal experimentation? Why or why not?

3. How does one determine whether or not abortion is a moral issue?

4. What effect do you think that the Supreme Court decision on abortion will have on our society? On the Mennonite Church?

Life and Values has been designed as a reading book or as an elective study in the Sunday school curriculum. For class activities see page 111. Its division into thirteen lessons provides for a full quarter of study; but adapting the course to fit time and interest should not be difficult. For instance, a group might want to spend only six weeks on the study or it might be interested only in abortion.

Much has been published on the subject of life and values. Some of these resources are listed under "Books and Magazine Articles."

In addition to the materials included in this booklet, resource persons are available in various geographical areas of the United States and Canada. Your district conference, Mennonite Board of Congregational Ministries, or Commission on Home

Ministries is prepared to help locate these person resources. These people can help plan the studies as well as take part in the study.

The credit for this book goes to all who contributed material and to those who saw the need to make it available in this form.

Edwin and Helen Alderfer

Introduction

This study guide grew out of current Christian concern about the ethical and religious implications of using modern medical technology as it affects the value of human life. The Mennonite Medical Association recognized a growing apprehension about getting more involved in the termination, prolongation, and control of the processes of life. It also considered the increased popularity of demanding medical services that effect the status of human life, especially the demands for abortion.

At its annual convention in 1972 the ethical issues of abortion and euthanasia were explored in the light of known values of human life. From this it was agreed that a Christian position must finally rest on biblical considerations. Subsequently a seminar on Human Life and Human Values was conducted with doctors and theologians participating. The findings at this meeting called for a consideration of the practical implications of abortion. For this additional study a conference was arranged on the same subject with doctors, nurses, chaplains, social workers, hospital administrators, and pastors participating. The papers, responses, and recorded discussions of these events were used as a basis for the preparation of this study manual. The editors have done well in selecting, condensing, and distilling pertinent information and suggestions from the resources made available through these and other media.

Life and Values does not provide the reader or a study group with ready-made answers. It does ask many of the right questions. It projects the factors involved in these issues. These factors need to be taken into consideration before making a decision about abortion, fetal experimentation, test-tube fertilization, or euthanasia. What is very important in the process of ethical reflection on these matters is to keep in sharp focus a respect for human life and personhood as they relate to the will of God.

John R. Mumaw
Executive Secretary
Mennonite Medical Association

More Truth and Light

I am confident
  the Lord hath more truth
  and light
Yet to break forth
  out of His word.
        John Robinson (to the Pilgrim's)

1. Biblical Statements on the Origin of Life (Part 1)

BY PAUL M. LEDERACH

The Concept of Life in Creation

The Genesis story, especially chapters 1 and 2, focuses one's attention on the concept of life in creation. Chapter 1 sets forth God's creative activity in six days. On the seventh day, He rested. The story of Creation climaxes with a great theological affirmation (Genesis 2:1-3) concerning the Sabbath.

Genesis 2 also tells a creation story. Instead of a series of creative acts extending through six days, it begins with the creation of man. Next God plants a garden and places man in that garden. As man tills the soil and keeps the garden, God notices that it is not good for him to be alone. So God decides to prepare a helper. God makes the animals, but none of these is able to "answer back" to Adam. Finally, God puts Adam to sleep, takes a rib from his side and creates a woman. When Adam sees the woman, he cries, "This at last is bone of my bones and flesh of my flesh" (2:23). As the first story of creation culminates in a great theological affirmation, so does the second. In the second the affirmation concerns marriage, "Therefore a man leaves his father and his mother and cleaves to his wife, and they become one flesh" (2:24).

In both Genesis 1 and 2, human beings are at the apex of God's creative activity. In Genesis 1, this is expressed by man's being the climax of creation. In Genesis 2, it is expressed by placing man in the center of God's creative activity.

Throughout Genesis 1 and 2, there are frequent references to life. The waters brought forth "living creatures" (1:20). The earth brought forth "living creatures" (1:24) — cattle and creeping things. Finally, God said, "Let us make man in our image" (1:26). In Genesis 2:7 we read, "The Lord God formed man of dust from the ground, and breathed into his nostrils the breath of life; and man became a living being."

"God formed, i.e., literally fashioned, molded (LXX *eplasen*, cf. plastic) man. The word also describes the work of a potter. Man is a combination of dust (which becomes his body) and divine breath (which is life) which is love breathed into him to make him a living being and is withdrawn to cause him to die (Psalm 104:29). The Lord God is directly responsible for the two constituents of man's being. He molds the first human body, and breathes His own uncreated breath into the molded body. Not even Genesis 1 is as direct and immediate as this, for God's hands at work in modeling and His mouth at work in breathing and not merely His Word (1:26) are here involved Man came into being by an act of God, and is a being sustained by the breath of God. Without God, man does not begin, and only with God does man continue to be.

"There is, however, another side to the story. Man is formed from the dust of the ground, but the Hebrew makes the connection even closer. Man and ground in Hebrew are *'adham* and *'adhamah* (sing. fem. noun; indeed the fem. form of man). The meaning of the word is not known, but man is certainly earthborn, made out of the substance known as the dust of the earth." [1]

In Genesis 1 human life transcends both material existence and other forms of life. Plants and living animals are in an intermediate relationship to God. They were brought forth by the water and by the earth in response to God's command. When it came to human life, God said, "Let us make man." A marked contrast is intended between that which is called into being by the *Word* of God — the *Word* that separated the waters, that brought light into being, that commanded the dry land to appear, and commanded the earth to bring forth vegetation and living creatures — and that which is molded and made into man, or as we read in Genesis 2 of God's breathing into man's nostrils the breath of life. Though life

---

1. G. Henton Davies, "Genesis," *The Broadman Bible Commentary*, Volume 1, p. 135.

in animals and man seems to be much the same, Paul reflected this idea of difference in 1 Corinthians 15:39 when he wrote, "For not all flesh is alike, but there is one kind for men, another for animals, another for birds, and another for fish."

Genesis 1 does little to define God's nature or the essence of man. The data are sparse; man is to be created in "our image, after our likeness." The word "image" *(tselem)* suggests a carved or hewn statue, or a copy of something else. "Likeness" *(demuth)* suggests a facsimile. These words do not imply that man is divine, rather he is copied after the Divine One with some of His attributes and he functions in many ways that are like God's. When God said, "Let us make man in our image, after our likeness," He suggested that He is the prototype or the "original" of man. It is not life as such that separates man from the rest of the living creatures, rather it is man's image of God and likeness to God.

"Image occurs approximately seventeen times in the Old Testament. In ten instances it refers to concrete objects such as a statue. It appears five times in the early chapters of Genesis. Perhaps we should note them:

Genesis 1:26	"Let us make man in our *image*."
Genesis 1:27	"So God created man in his own *image*, in the *image* of God he created him; male and female he created them."
Genesis 5:3	"When Adam had lived a hundred and thirty years, he became the father of a son in his own *likeness*, after his *image*, and named him Seth."
Genesis 9:6	"Whoever sheds the blood of man, by man shall his blood be shed; for God made man in his own *image*."

If "image" suggests a literal, physical resemblance, "likeness" has a tendency to temper the emphasis on the physical and to suggest something more abstract, such as spiritual, or personality, or self-consciousness, or free will, or moral capacity. Though we generally emphasize that the image of God does not refer to the physical primarily, yet we cannot exclude this possibility, especially in the light of the fluctuating point of view in the Old Testament concerning God — at one place suggesting that God can be seen, and in another that He cannot be seen. It is clear that man cannot make an image of God, but God did indeed make man an image of Himself.

It is interesting to note that in Genesis 1:26 God made man in "our image, after our likeness" whereas in Genesis 5:3 Seth was in Adam's likeness and after his image. The order of the words is reversed suggesting something of interchangeability, and cautioning against too sharp a delineation between the terms.

In Genesis 1:26, 27 both men and women are said to be created in the image of God. This is an important observation in that it refutes the pagan notions of cultures surrounding Israel that man was patterned after a god and woman after a goddess.

The witness of the Bible is that God is life. He is the living Father; He is the source of life. For example, John 5:26: "For as the Father has life in himself, so he has granted the Son also to have life in himself." Life in origin and in manifestation is in God's hands. The Bible claims that God not only gives life but also takes life. When God withdraws breath or spirit, creatures die. See Job 4:9; 34:14; Psalm 104:29; Isaiah 38:17; Deuteronomy 5:25.

In addition to breath as a carrier of life, the Bible also considers blood as a vehicle for life. After the flood, God reestablished a covenant with mankind through Noah. In Genesis 9:3-6, God said,

> "Every moving thing that lives shall be food for you; and as I gave you the green plants, I give you everything. Only you shall not eat flesh with its life, that is, its blood. For your life-blood I will surely require a reckoning; of every beast I will require it and of man; of every man's brother I will require the life of man. Whoever sheds the blood of man, by man shall his blood be shed; for God made man in his own image."

That life is in the blood is restated in Leviticus 17:11, 12,

> "For the life of the flesh is in the blood; and I have given it for you upon the altar to make atonement for your souls; for it is the blood that makes atonement, by reason of the life.

Therefore I have said to the people of Israel, No person among you shall eat blood."

Again in verse 14,

"For the life of every creature is the blood of it; therefore I have said to the people of Israel, You shall not eat the blood of any creature, for the life of every creature is its blood."

When Genesis 9:4-6 is placed beside Leviticus 17:10-14 (the life of the flesh is in the blood), it is seen that life is basically the same in all creatures, whether in man or in animals. Here the life is in the blood. That which makes human life different is that God made man in His own image.

In summary, concerning the origin of life in the context of creation, observe that:

1. Life has its origin in God who is life.
2. Life is life; life is shared by all the living creatures created by God.
3. Life is considered as inbreathed; it is also considered to be in the blood.
4. That man was created in the image and likeness of God; this is what distinguished human life from other life.

Questions

1. What is the meaning of the phrase "in our image" in Genesis 1:26?
2. What value, if any, does being made in "the image of God" place upon a human life?
3. Human life is said to be the same and different from other forms of life. What are the similarities and the differences according to the Bible?
4. If the Bible says that God gives and takes life, does it follow that we should never interfere with God's "schedule?"

2. Biblical Statements on the Origin of Life (Part 2)

BY PAUL M. LEDERACH

The Beginning of Human Life in Procreation

It may be helpful to approach this issue by listing a number of references that bear on the subject.

Genesis 5:3: "When Adam had lived a hundred and thirty years, he became the father of a son in his own likeness, after his image, and named him Seth."

Genesis 25:21: "And Isaac prayed to the Lord for his wife, because she was barren; and the Lord granted his prayer, and Rebekah his wife conceived. The children struggled together within her; and she said, 'If it is thus, why do I live?' So she went to inquire of the Lord. And the Lord said to her,
'Two nations are in your womb,
   and two peoples, born of you, shall be divided;
the one shall be stronger than the other,
   the elder shall serve the younger.' "

Exodus 21:22-25: "When men strive together, and hurt a woman with child, so that there is a miscarriage, and yet no harm follows, the one who hurt her shall be fined, according as the woman's husband shall lay upon him; and he shall pay as the judges determine. If any harm follows, then you shall give life for life, eye for eye, tooth for tooth, hand for hand, foot for foot, burn for burn, wound for wound, stripe for stripe."

1 Samuel 4:19: "Now his daughter-in-law, the wife of Phinehas, was with child, about to give birth. And when she heard the tidings that the ark of God was captured, and that her

father-in-law and her husband were dead, she bowed and gave birth; for her pains came upon her."

Job 3:16: " 'Or why was I not as a hidden untimely birth, as infants that never see the light?' "

Job 10:8, 18, 19: " 'Thy hands fashioned and made me; and now thou dost turn about and destroy me. Why didst thou bring me forth from the womb? Would that I had died before any eye had seen me, and were as though I had not been, carried from the womb to the grave.' "

Psalm 139:13-16:
"For thou didst form my inward parts,
   thou didst knit me together in my mother's womb.
I praise thee, for thou art fearful and wonderful.
   Wonderful are thy works!
Thou knowest me right well;
   my frame was not hidden from thee,
when I was being made in secret,
   intricately wrought in the depths of the earth.
Thy eyes beheld my unformed substance;
   in thy book were written, every one of them,
the days that were formed for me,
   when as yet there was none of them."

Ecclesiastes 6:3-6: "If a man begets a hundred children, and lives many years, so that the days of his years are many, but he does not enjoy life's good things, and also has no burial, I say that an untimely birth is better off than he. For it comes into vanity and goes into darkness, and in darkness its name is covered; moreover it has not seen the sun or known anything; yet it finds rest rather than he. Even though he should live a thousand years twice told, yet enjoy no good — do not all go to the one place?"

Isaiah 49:1, 5: "The Lord called me from the womb, from the body of my mother he named my name. . . . And now the Lord says, who formed me from the womb to be his servant. . . ."

Jeremiah 1:5: " 'Before I formed you in the womb I knew you, and before you were born I consecrated you; I appointed you a prophet to the nations.' "

Luke 1:15: "'And he will be filled with the Holy Spirit, even from his mother's womb.'"

Luke 1:41: "And when Elizabeth heard the greeting of Mary, the babe leaped in her womb; and Elizabeth was filled with the Holy Spirit."

Luke 1:44: "'For behold, when the voice of your greeting came to my ears, the babe in my womb leaped for joy.'"

John 1:12, 13: "But to all who received him, who believed in his name, he gave power to become children of God; who were born, not of blood nor of the will of the flesh nor of the will of man, but of God."

John 3:6: "'That which is born of the flesh is flesh, and that which is born of the Spirit is spirit.'"

Genesis 1 does not present the ability of procreation as a matter of course. It is presented as a divine blessing. God, who is the source of life, blessed mankind and told them to be fruitful and multiply and to fill the earth (v. 28).

In Genesis 25:21-24, it is clear that God was aware of the unborn children in the womb of Rebekah. The struggle between the children became so great that Rebekah despaired of living. In her misery she inquired of the Lord. Note that the Lord was aware of these unborn infants, and told Rebekah about their future and about their natures.

Likewise in the cases of Isaiah 49:1, 5 and of Jeremiah 1:5, even before birth God was aware of these men and of their potentialities.

It is particularly striking to hear what God said about Jeremiah — that He formed him (like the potter's shaping of a vessel, recalling Genesis 2:7); that before Jeremiah was born God knew him (the word "know" means firsthand contact between two personalities); that before Jeremiah was born he was consecrated or appointed for a mission (before he was born, as a fetus his life was claimed by God). It is interesting to remember also that Jeremiah did not want to be a prophet; he was not really reconciled to his calling; and he expressed contempt for those who eagerly and often unthinkingly seized upon the office of prophet (Jeremiah 23:16-22).

In the Sermon on the Mount (Matthew 6:25-34), Jesus emphasized that God was deeply concerned about men and their needs, that if God takes care of birds and grass, how much more will He care for His children? These references to Jacob and Esau, to Jeremiah, and Isaiah *before birth* suggest that God is aware of unborn humans, of their personalities and potential.

Psalm 139 takes this idea a bit further. The psalmist suggests that the eyes of God beheld him in his unformed state, and that God had a detailed knowledge of every day of his life, even before he was born! Can this claim be made by every man? If so, in the light of this what prescience is needed to jeopardize the life of a fetus or the life of a mature human?

Exodus 21:22, for some, suggests a distinction between a fully developed human life and the life of a fetus. There is, however, controversy concerning the commonly accepted interpretation. From this passage it is inferred that the fetus was not considered a human life, or "life for life" would have been demanded for its death as it was for the mother's life, or at least a fetus for fetus as required in surrounding cultures.

The case is simply this. Two men are fighting. The wife of one intervenes and gets hurt. If the woman is pregnant and loses her child, the man who hurt her indemnified the husband for the fetus by paying a sum fixed by him and approved by the judges. Since the death of the child is accidental, the death penalty is not imposed. However, if further harm resulted, such as the death of the woman, the death penalty was applicable unless it could be proven the act was unintentional.

Most modern translations use the word miscarriage in verse 22. Jack W. Cottrell in *Christianity Today* (March 16, 1973) questions this, "The interpretation of this passage most faithful to the text is that which distinguished between a premature birth (not miscarriage) that harms neither the mother nor the child and a premature birth in which one or the other is injured or even dies. In the latter case the life of the fetus is valued just as highly as the life of the mother, and the *lex talionis* (eye for eye) principle applies to both. There is absolutely no warrant for concluding . . . that in this passage 'in contrast to the mother, the fetus is not reckoned as a soul.' . . . At the very least, if this view of Exodus 21:22-25 is correct, then one can no longer find a biblical justification for liberalizing abortion laws."

Ecclesiastes 6:3-6 and 1 Corinthians 15:8 also deal with miscarriage or "untimely birth." In Bible times a birth which occurred before the full gestation period was regarded as fallen or miscarried regardless of whether the fetus was nonviable or capable of independent existence. Sometimes the miscarriage occurred because of a crisis, as in 1 Samuel 4:19. Job expressed the wish that he would have been miscarried as an infant that never saw the light. In Job 10:8, appear the familiar ideas of being fashioned in the mother's womb and of being made of clay and returning to dust again. But in 10:18 Job asks why he had not been miscarried, had died before any eye had seen him; for having died in that state, Job thought it would have been as though "I had not been." He simply would have been carried from the womb to the grave! Job's complaint, however, is the voice of human despair; his view is hardly to be equated with that of the psalmist experiencing and confident in God's presence.

Ecclesiastes with its typical, pessimistic notes speaks of the miscarried infant as coming into vanity and going into darkness without a name, without having seen the sun or known anything. The writer adds that even so, the person experiencing an untimely birth goes to the same place as the one who has lived a long life.

The Apostle Paul's reference to an untimely birth or miscarriage is unusual (1 Corinthians 15:8). The Greek word is *ektroma*. Paul may have used the word to refer to his unusual entrance into Christianity. The miscarriage of Judaism, an alien moribund mother, precipitated his transformation from persecutor to apostle. I prefer to think Paul referred to his apostleship. The figure of an untimely birth illustrated that he is no more worthy of the name of apostle than an aborted fetus is worthy of the name of a child. Clearly, if Paul's use of the term provides an insight into his feelings about a fetus (and here we may be abusing the data), his view is quite different from those expressed about Jacob and Esau, about Jeremiah and Isaiah. We can scarcely go much further than to say that having come to full term, persons like Jeremiah went on to fulfill God's purposes for them. Whereas those who experienced untimely death, without name, without breath, without having seen the light of day, moved simply from the womb to the grave.

The references in John suggest that whatever the fetus is, it is the product of the union of male and female humans. This is the sense behind the words of Jesus (John 3:6). Though the contrast is between physical birth and spiritual rebirth, yet the implication is clear — that which is born of the flesh is flesh, that which is conceived by humans is human, and as such has value, fundamentally, because of God's image.

Luke's record of John the Baptist's birth is very interesting. In this case the unborn infant is not only filled with the Holy Spirit, but is also aware of what is going on outside the womb! He was filled with joy at the voice of Mary. Apparently, this occurred six months after John was conceived by natural generation.

In summary, Bible passages that refer to the beginning of human life in procreation suggest:

1. The unborn fetus has value (Exodus 21:22).
2. The fetus is wrought by God and known by God (Psalm 139:13-16; Isaiah 49:1, 5; Jeremiah 1:5).
3. The fetus can be called by God (Jeremiah 1:5).
4. It is possible for the fetus to be filled with the Spirit (Luke 1:15).
5. The fetus is human. That which is born of the flesh is flesh (John 3:6).
6. The status of the infant that miscarries is not clear. There is the suggestion that the miscarried infant has no name, has not seen the sun, and moves from the womb to the grave (Ecclesiastes 6:3-6; Job 10:18).
7. God is aware of who a person is and what he will do, even before birth (Psalm 139).

Humanness

It is possible to go to the Creation story and to discern characteristics of what it is to be human. A number of these are often listed:

To be human is to have dominion, to create, to control, to name, to explore.

To be human is to have the power of moral decision, to think, and to plan, to see and to decide.

To be human is to appreciate beauty.

To be human is to join with God in the ability to work.

To be human is to enjoy interpersonal relationships. God saw that it was not good for man to be alone.

To be human is to be able to take voluntary action.

To be human is to worship, to be able to interact with God.

In the New Testament two passages perpetuate the idea of humanness, drawn largely from the creation narratives. These are found in 1 Corinthians 11:7: "For a man ought not to cover his head, since he is the *image* and glory of God," and in James 3:9: "With it [the tongue] we bless the Lord and Father, and with it we curse men, who are made in the likeness of God."

In the New Testament the revelation of God in Christ seems to obliterate the thought of man in the image of God, rather Jesus is seen as the image of God. Jesus is the perfect correspondence with the divine prototype.

Jesus is the new man. Adam was merely a foreshadowing type.

"No one has ever seen God; the only Son, who is in the bosom of the Father, he has made him known" (John 1:18).

"And he who sees me sees him who sent me" (John 12:45).

"He who has seen me has seen the Father" (John 14:9).

"He is the image of the invisible God" (Colossians 1:15).

"To keep them from seeing the light of the gospel of the glory of Christ, who is the likeness of God" (2 Corinthians 4:4).

In the light of the Christ event, a theology of humanness no longer springs from an analysis of the Creation account; rather it springs from a knowledge of Jesus Christ. Jesus came not only to reveal God to man, but also Jesus came to make known what man is to be like — man as God intended. To be human is to be like Jesus.

The message of the gospel is that persons to be fully human are to be transformed or made like Jesus. This is not to say that an adult non-Christian is not human, only that he has not fully realized his humanity in Christ.

"Put on the new nature, which is being renewed in knowledge after the image of its creator. Here there cannot be Greek and Jew, circumcised and uncircumcised, barbarian, Scythian, slave, free man, but Christ is all, and in all" (Colossians 3:10, 11).

"Put off your old nature which belongs to your former manner of life and is corrupt through deceitful lusts, and be renewed in the spirit of your minds, and put on the new nature, created after the likeness of God in true righteousness and holiness" (Ephesians 4:22-24).

"For those whom he foreknew he also predestined to be conformed to the image of his Son" (Romans 8:29).

"Just as we have borne the image of the man of dust, we shall also bear the image of the man of heaven" (1 Corinthians 15:49).

"And we all, with unveiled face, beholding the glory of the Lord, are being changed into his likeness from one degree of glory to another; for this comes from the Lord who is the Spirit" (2 Corinthians 3:18).

"Beloved, we are God's children now; it does not yet appear what we shall be, but we know that when he appears we shall be like him, for we shall see him as he is" (1 John 3:2).

A theology of humanness begins in redemption. Paul wrote that God "saved us and called us with a holy calling, not in virtue of our works but in virtue of his own purpose and the grace which he gave us in Christ Jesus ages ago, and now has manifested through the appearing of our Savior Christ Jesus, who abolished death and brought life and immortality to light through the gospel" (2 Timothy 1:9, 10). Jesus brought the *true life* to light. Natural life is no longer thought of as something less perfect, which is to be perfected; rather life in the flesh, or humanness characterized by fallenness, is seen as the perversion of the divine intention. Through Jesus, human life is renewed and regenerated and is made as God intended. The true life that Jesus revealed moves from that of having dominion, to that of being servant. It moves from voluntary self-centered action to that of mission.

It is important to observe that this Jesus, as revelation of

God, in His incarnation was conceived of the Holy Spirit. He was a fetus. He was born of the Virgin Mary. He grew physically, socially, intellectually, and spiritually. Humanness is no longer defined from the standpoint of creation and of Adam but from the coming of the new Adam. To become like Jesus is not only to become like God — the image and likeness restored — but also to become the kind of human being that God intended. The gospel received makes true humanness possible.

We do' not fully know what it is to be human. But we do know that the form that Jesus took is the form in which God intended humanness to be expressed. We also know that the human form that Jesus took was typical of the kind of men God intended to save through Jesus' death and resurrection. The life that Jesus lived makes clear God's intention for humanness. But our understanding of such humanness is only partial; it will be complete when He appears again. Then we will see Him and be made like Him.

In summary in developing a theology of humanness:

1. We can discern characteristics of humanness from the Creation stories.
2. A theology of humanness, however, begins with redemption; with Jesus, rather than with Adam.
3. Jesus, the Son of God, became a human being to reveal God to humans, and to reveal God's intention for human beings.
4. What Jesus became in the incarnation is representative of the humanity that God loves and God wants to save.
5. In the incarnation Jesus experienced all the stages of human growth and development from conception and birth to death and resurrection. In the New Testament the image of God does not belong to man so much as to Jesus Christ, and through a faith relationship to Him the believer is transformed into the same image. This is both a hope and a reality.

Simply stated, a theology of humanness is to be Christlike.

Questions

1. What, to you, is the significance of God's awareness of the

unborn fetus as recorded in Genesis 25:21; Jeremiah 1:5; Luke 1:15?

2. What is the significance of the words "personhood" and "humanness" in the discussion of abortion?

3. What to you are the most distinctive qualities of humanness?

4. How does a theology of humanness that is rooted in Christlikeness inform one's views of abortion?

5. If to be fully human is to be "transformed or made like Jesus," would it follow then that an unborn fetus, for example is not fully human?

3. The Religious Perspective on Abortion

BY ROSS T. BENDER

1. What Is the Question?

What is the question we are addressing? Specifically it has to do with the rightness or the ethical advisability of a therapeutic abortion.

I am asserting that the question is not usually "When does the fetus become human?" This question is posed with the assumption that if the point can be established after which the fetus is human and before which it is something else, an abortion can be performed with a clear conscience up until that point on the line.

This question is fruitless for the resolution of the problem for several reasons:

(1) It does not provide us with a universally accepted definition of what constitutes humanness which can be applied.

(2) It assumes a point of time after which it would be clear that no ethical questions could be raised if the abortion is performed prior to that point, or conversely that all abortions are ethically wrong after that point. This argument provides us with no articulate ethical framework by which to make a judgment.

"When is humanness?" is also a fruitless question. It is fruitless because definitions of humanness proceed from our observations of the fully developed person; to make a comparison with the fetus of such observations would force us to conclude that the fetus is something less than human.

When Does the Soul Enter the Body?

The answer here is not susceptible of scientific investigation since the soul is not an entity which can be observed and measured. Nor can we find a biblical answer to this question since it presupposes something that the Bible does not, that soul and body are distinguishable. In biblical thought they are a unity so that it is biblically correct to say that man *is* a living soul, rather than that he *has* one.

Does the Conceptus Consist of Individual Uniqueness or Is It Simply the Mother's Tissue?

It is sometimes argued that the conceptus being parasitic in character (i.e. feeding on the mother and unable to survive apart from that total dependency) is part of the mother's body. Its destiny should be determined exclusively by the mother, who has the sole right (legally and morally) to determine whether it shall survive or be aborted.

In considering this question, we do well to make several distinctions. If the conceptus is thought to be the mother's tissue, in what sense is it like the rest of her tissue? If it is similar to other healthy tissue, then it is clear that she is no more at liberty to excise this tissue than that tissue simply at her pleasure. If it is like a tumor, we must conclude that pregnancy is a disease, yet not even associating pregnancy with morning sickness makes pregnancy per se a disease. It is a healthy and normal function of the female body and not evidence of pathology.

While the Christian community is vitally interested in the question of the legal rights and responsibilities of the fetus, we must not confuse what is legal and what is morally right.

Is Abortion the Moral Equivalent of Homicide or Killing in War?

There are those who answer immediately "yes" and insist on using such emotionally loaded words as murder and homicide to describe the event and on such warmly human words as child or baby instead of such clinically cold terms as *zygote, conceptus, embryo,* or *fetus.* In my judgment, these words serve a rhetorical purpose better than a logical one and appeal to the feelings more than to the reason.

There may indeed be some similarities, in that one life (or is it a potential life?) is terminated by the action of another. But there are some fundamental differences as well both in terms of the social context of the action and the motivation for it. The act of murder or of war involves relatively equal contending parties who are in conflict over some issue, relationship, or property. The conflict generates a greater than normal degree of hostility which in turn leads to an act of violence perpetrated by one upon the other or by both parties against each other. One can only label a minor surgical procedure as an act of violence by stretching the meaning of the term way out of shape. Nor is the act of effecting an abortion necessarily an act of personal hostility toward the fetus; it may be based on other motivations (even though the motivation is wrong).

2. What Is the Problem for Which Abortion Is the Answer?

The problem is in its simplest terms an unwanted pregnancy. Our exploration must now take us into the meaning of the term "unwanted" and how this situation came into being that a pregnancy is unwanted.

Birth Control

It may be unwanted because the mother has "enough" children and cannot "afford" any more. The terms "enough" and "afford" must be placed in quotation marks since they have a very elastic and imprecise meaning and are for the most part highly subjective in their usage. As such they do not provide the Christian community with an adequate basis on which to make an ethical judgment. To make a decision to secure an abortion for economic reasons is not an adequate Christian reason. The Christian faith also has an ethical concern about economics, including such matters as valuing people above things and sharing this world's goods with those who are in need. Responsible parenthood and family planning call for decision and action before conception rather than afterward.

Illicit Intercourse

It may be that the pregnant woman is unwed or that the

father is not her husband. The pregnancy under these circumstances is understandably an embarrassment. We must question, however, whether an abortion is the redemptive corrective that is needed in the situation. The world may see abortion as a solution with merit to an unfortunate problem but the Christian community does not advocate short-circuiting and avoidance as the solution but repentance, forgiveness, and reconciliation.

Involuntary Intercourse

If the pregnancy is the result of forced intercourse (such as rape or incest), should the woman therefore be expected to carry the resulting fetus to full term on the assumption that it is in some sense God's gift to her?

Medical reports indicate that the incidence of such cases is fairly insignificant from a statistical point of view. They represent the exceptional cases to which individual answers must be found. However, to proceed with an abortion on the assumption that an abortion in itself will solve the problem is not enough.

Social Control of "Undesirable" Population

Social engineering is not based on Christian standards of who has worth and who does not. It is based rather on self-serving considerations whereby the privileged group in society which controls the levers of power and influence exercises its will upon the less privileged. Therefore, this issue has no place in a Christian consideration of the rightness or wrongness of abortion but must be ruled totally out of order.

Physical and/or Mental Disability

While the law of the survival of the fittest may be an appropriate principle of evolution in the animal world, I believe that mankind is at its best when it comes to the defense of the weakest and most helpless of its number. The capacity for compassion is elicited in the presence of human frailty and dependence. I believe too that compassion must be extended to the mother and the family of the handicapped person and that creative ways can and must be found in the Christian community to share their burden.

Mental Retardation

If a given couple is sufficiently mature to receive the blessing of the church on that marriage, they may likewise be sufficiently capable of bearing and rearing a child. If not, consideration might be given to sterilization or other forms of birth control.

If the case involves the pregnancy of a retarded unmarried woman, it may be similar to unwanted pregnancies resulting from involuntary intercourse and therefore, treated as such.

Medical or Psychiatric Reasons

There are, it is clear, some medical circumstances which require a medical judgment about the relative danger to the mother's life or health of permitting the fetus to develop to maturity as over against aborting it. *Those circumstances would give consent to* the doctor to proceed with the abortion rather than to imperil the mother's life. He would do so simply on the basis that the mother's life is to be valued above that of the potential life as yet unknown and unnamed. She has a personal history and an established place in her family and community.

These cases are a very small part of the total population of today's therapeutic abortions. By far the largest number are sought on psychiatric grounds. While these constitute a legal basis for proceeding, can the Christian community say that they are sufficient moral grounds for the abortion? Families faced with an unwanted pregnancy need competent counselors and a compassionate community to help them see that abortion is not the only answer. However, to take an absolutist position is to cut ourselves off from the possibility of being helpful.

3. What Are Some Religious Perspectives on the Question?

We have now reduced the scope of the question before us to a very narrow focus. We are not talking about abortion on demand under any and every circumstance. In my view, the only major problematic area calling for ethical deliberation in decision-making involves those cases requiring a psychiatric judgment. In those few instances involving rape or incest, the same considerations and procedures should apply since these do involve the emotional health and well-being of the girl or woman who has been violated, physically and emotionally. All others are ruled out in advance since they are based on inadequate (from a Christian perspective) grounds. Those few cases involving the mother's physical health or very life call for a strictly medical judgment.

On Freedom and Responsibility

While it is true that man is created in the image of God and for fellowship with God, the Bible, both in the Old and New Testaments, sees man also as part and parcel of the natural created order (Genesis 2:7; 3:19), whereas God, the Creator, stands above and over against the world of nature which He brought into being by the Word of His command.

But to see man *only* from the point of view of his being bound to nature — of coming from the ground and returning to it — is from the Judeo-Christian point of view to miss something important. To be created in the image of God is to be a spiritual being, a being for whom such matters as *freedom, choice, purpose, value, responsibility* become important aspects of his everyday living. We can only talk about moral responsibility if we believe that man stands not only within nature like a tree or an animal but also, like his Maker, in some sense stands over against it and above it.

On History and Social Experience

Just as the physical sciences have underscored man's basic connection and interdependence with the world of nature, so the biological sciences have made us aware of the physical and structural relationships between man and the animals. To say that man is an animal, in the biological sense, is not an insult. But to say that man is *just* an animal is to make a serious mistake. One of the questions which has persisted in the discussion of the relationship between man and the animals is not only, How is man similar to the animals? but, How is he different?

To put the matter theologically, the uniqueness of man does not lie first of all in the ability to stand up or to think straight. It lies rather in his *obligation* and his *destiny*. Man is a moral being, with a conscience. Man is responsible and personal, not an animal or a thing. Now that the earth has been adequately peopled, it is time for man to reflect whether God's desire is that he should go on breeding indiscriminately like the animal world where the checks and balances of nature take care of the problems of excessive population *or* whether God wants him to exercise his moral, intellectual and emotional powers (which are also God-given) to see to it that those who are born can be properly taken care of.

On Making Decisions

Man's sense of responsibility is grounded in the fact that he is addressed by God. It is because man is made in the image of God that God can address him, put a question to him to which he must respond with a yes or a no, have conversation with him, as it were.

There is a basic *Yes* or *No* that has to do with a person's orientation toward God, toward himself, toward his brother, toward his neighbor, toward life. Every day that *Yes* or *No* is tested in all the big and little issues he confronts and the decisions he makes. Will he confront those issues and make those decisions out of a selfish self-centered orientation or will he make them for the honor and glory of God?

We are faced with decisions that in former years man left to God alone in terms of the well-being and destiny of all that He has created, including human life. We accept with joy our power to be procreators of human life through the exercise of our sexual powers and in this way acknowledge our partnership with God in creation. But we shrink with horror from the thought of sharing with God in determining if and when a potential life shall be given the opportunity to develop or be turned aside. It is well that we hesitate, for we know something of man's self-centeredness as well as his tendency to play God in these matters, that is to say, to usurp the role that belongs to God alone.

To hold such great power in our hands is to be charged with great responsibility. We must exercise that power humbly, with restraint and sensitivity, and also with gratitude that God has entrusted it to us. It is possible to know the mind of Christ in these matters and to sense the presence of the Spirit of God even though one cannot *in every case* know in advance what is called for without knowing the details of the situation.

While the procedures for coming to decision and the issues which take precedence will vary from case to case, there is one consideration which in my judgment is indispensable. It is that the decision not be made by the mother (and father) alone since individualism undercuts the very nerve of Christian decision-making. Granted, not everyone in a given congregation can participate in such deliberations, but the congregation can be represented by mature brothers and sisters who can share in formulating the decision and in assuming responsibility for it. This is more than a safeguard against arbitrary ill-advised action; it is a recognition of the biblical principle that if one member suffers, the whole body suffers.

On Creative Alternatives

Arising out of the above consideration that we are a body, does it not follow that one creative alternative is to see the problem not simply as *her* problem, but as *our* problem? This calls as a minimum for leaving off finger-pointing and breast-beating. If the person(s) in crisis felt the Christian community as a supportive body rather than a self-righteous one, many of the social and psychiatric problems would be solved in themselves or at the least be significantly mitigated. Social stigma and disgrace would be replaced by social caring and rehabilitation. Many problems of anxiety are resolved when one is lovingly surrounded by a caring-sharing community of which one is a part. Emotional, physical, and even economic burdens are not intended to be borne alone but are to be shared by brothers and sisters whose burden is lighter for the time being. The world must resort to short circuit answers because the rule is every one for himself. That must not become the rule of life in the body of Christ nor may we resort to strategies that reflect or encourage this rule.

I would like to see a strategy of having a small group of persons surrounding the person(s) in crisis and helping them in working through their decision with the physician. Their function then would be to stand by irrespective of the direction of the decision. If the decision is to terminate the pregnancy, their role can be to minister the grace and compassion of

Christ for as long as emotional and physical healing require. If the decision is to continue the pregnancy, their role is the same with the additional responsibilities of following through in helping to make a home for the child where he/she can receive the needed nurture (whether with the mother or in another home) and in helping to create an appropriate climate for the mother to regain her strength and rebuild her life.

Questions

1. What are the factors that determine who in our world shall survive?
2. How is it possible that what is legal may not be morally right?
3. What are the religious factors upon which you base your view on abortion?
4. What considerations need to be kept in mind when a family in the church is facing the pregnancy of an unmarried daughter or the involvement of a son in such a pregnancy, when it is suggested that in the Christian community we "bear one another's burdens"?
5. How can the Christian concepts of freedom and responsibility be exercised by an individual member within the Christian community without destroying community or personal integrity?

4. The Eternal Nature of Life

BY JOHN R. MUMAW

The expressed will of God for man in the Genesis story is an indication of Divine intent to give high priority to human life. Man is the divine agent to execute affairs on earth.

1. Management of Human Life Is Regulated by Divine Purpose

The question we face in this discussion is whether or not the dominion God has assigned to man includes the management of human life. Historically "the Christian prohibition of abortion was made on the principle of inviolability of human-formed life, whose beginning and end involves an act of God."[1]

From the Protestant viewpoint it has been assumed that moral issues are to be resolved on the basis of biblical principles and human judgment. Smith quotes Robert E. Fitch as saying, "There is a Catholic strength, its name is order. There is a Catholic sickness, its name is tyranny. There is a Protestant strength, and its name is liberty. There is a Protestant sickness and its name is anarchy."[2] Perhaps we can add to that formula; there is an Anabaptist strength and its name is biblicism; and there is an Anabaptist sickness and its name is legalism. We are concerned to know what is the will of God regarding the management of human life and how to apply that knowledge in the practice of medicine and spiritual counseling.

2. Human Judgment Is Subject to Divine Purpose

Our problem centers in discovering the will of God. How do

we know God's intent for human life? At what point in the development of the fetus does that intention apply? It is difficult to be strictly theological in our approach to this issue. We have been confronted with so many humanistic influences that we have to exercise a vigorous spiritual discipline to find Christian answers. As with other moral issues, the child of God cannot find his solution in nature. He must look beyond himself and his environment to see the truth, the way, and the life. Any attempt to manage human life without reference to the Word of God opens the way for the influence of alien philosophies. The Christian can ill afford to rely upon a pagan view of life to order his behavior.

3. Personhood Identifies Purpose

Man was constituted with a personhood compatible with relationship to God. Creation established a race capable of expressing itself in reciprocal communication. It is within this context of relationship with God that we are best able to understand the humanity of man.

Man relates personally with God in fellowship and obedience. He is able to participate in the life of God and to respond to His will. It means that God created man with a view to having a sustained relationship in which eternal purposes could be fulfilled through human activity. The Scriptures are less explicit in reference to the inherent qualities of man's nature than in the description of his relationship. The decisive factor in identifying humanness in the fetus is not biological or anthropological but theological. We are forced to weigh the implications of having a life that is held sacred in its relationship to God.

It is important to remember that the Scriptures present a holistic view of man. Personhood rests primarily on the elements of spirit and soul. The spirit in this sense is the focal point of man's humanness. This does not mean, however, that man has a spiritual entity separate from his mind and body.[3] Paul Tournier addresses himself to the meaning of the person when he says, "In reality the spirit, the 'breath of life' which God breathed into the nostrils of man, became incarnate in the whole of the human animal, in his body as well as in his psyche or his mind; it animates all of them, it expresses itself in each of them."[4] If the spirit is the essence of the human person, as he asserts, then God's will for man is made known to that part of his being. The spirit in man responds to divine direction and uses the physiological and psychological functions to express itself. Any position on abortion must take into account this synthetic view of man. The termination of human life cuts off the channel of divine direction in human affairs.

4. Divine Revelation Establishes Purpose

The basic source in determining the Christian meaning of human life is divine revelation. It is the task of theology to translate the message of Scripture into the language of contemporary thought.

We are concerned with the biblical concept of man and the bearing such meanings may have on the question of abortion. We are reaching for methods of interpretation that will keep us in line with pure theological presuppositions and methodology. We do not intend here to draw up an apology to answer the Supreme Court, or to analyze secular systems of thought but to explore the meanings of divine revelation. What is the mind of God for the conduct of human life?

5. Purpose Determines Values

The testimony of Jesus puts human life into a category all its own. One soul is worth more than the whole world. Any valid explanation of this must give to man a high priority in the scheme of God's creation. He was created in the divine image.

This possibility of being in favorable relationship with God promises fellowship and providential purpose. It has a direct bearing on our estimate of human life. . . . More important than this is the discernment of God's will. The fact that God created man in His own likeness indicates an investment of Himself and puts the value of life at the top of the list over all other creatures. Human life has an inestimable value. Its purpose can be understood only in the context of this supreme worth.

We are the more impressed with the fact of human value when we consider the biblical concept that man is only slightly less than God both in regenerated human existence and in eternal essence. Psalm 8:4-6.

We have implied that finding God's purpose for human life demands an understanding of the value He places upon man. Cezar Heine has put it in the reverse order:

> The value of human life is also based on God's will. (God's will is an aspect of God's image in man, i.e. our relationship as creatures which obey their Creator). It is God who gives life and it is He who can take life again. God intends something with our lives. Life here on earth can be lived out in many ways, for example, in suffering or happiness, in great activity or enforced inactivity. However, life on earth is not the only life. There is also the life of the future. Therefore, even though our life on earth is the visible and obvious form (Genesis 9:6) of achieving what God wants with our lives, life is not absolute. God has the ultimate authority to end life here.[5]

The point at which a germinating life can claim to be a fit subject of protection for the preservation of its dignity remains for another study. Assuming, however, that it reaches that stage at the time when the first origins of individual life are established, we are led to regard fetal life as the object of that protection. We arrive at that conclusion with the understanding that the essential constitutive features of a human individual are present. It deserves being recognized as a person with its own genetic code and all the potential which that establishes.

6. Providence Engages Divine Purpose

We have yet another problem to be resolved. What of the pregnancies occurring from illicit intercourse? How do we attach God's will for a "rape" pregnancy? There is no easy answer to this and other cases in the category of "forced" experience. The perpetuation of God's will in marriage of male and female relies upon the mystical elements of affection. The will of God is that husband and wife shall have mutual delight and complementary strength in each other. And this is the order in which God intends the perpetuation of the race. When pregnancies occur outside of wedlock it becomes a case in which the process set in motion continues to affect God's purpose in spite of its having occurred outside of God's order.

It is the will of God to propagate the race within the bounds of valid marriage. Sexual morality is clearly defined in New Testament Scripture as having monogamous restrictions and mutual marital consent. Instead of supporting the use of abortion to resolve unwanted pregnancies the church should devote its energies to promoting social purity and marital unity.

Established standards of morality have exceptions, violations, and aberrations. When unwanted pregnancies occur under any of these circumstances it becomes an occasion for our understanding and compassion. A rigid position on abortion does not call for a harsh attitude toward the person or persons involved. At the point of having to decide whether or not to terminate the nascent life there is need for sympathetic counsel. The caring ministry of the church is extended to any person involved in such a predicament.

7. Stewardship of Life Conforms to Divine Purposes

There is a sense in which persons are responsible for control of their historical existence and destiny. For the Christian the crucial point is how to exercise that control within the bounds of the will of God. We must ascertain what is the divine intent for the life He gives. This more than the dignity of human being is a decisive factor in determining the morality of abortion.

The Christian fails or succeeds in his stewardship of life in proportion as he recognizes that it belongs to God and uses it to promote divine purposes. In a very real sense the Christian is not his own for he has been bought with a price.[6] While this refers particularly to the price of spiritual redemption the assessed value of man includes provision for the redemption of the body also. It indicates the will of God extends its range of concern to include what man does to human life. Its having an intrinsic value from creation is surpassed by the value it has in relation to God.

Human life is encased in a physical body. Even that is not our own but it belongs to another. God has given us our bodies as a trust. As Professor Ramsey says, life is "entirely an ordination, a loan, and a stewardship. His essence is his existence before God and to God, and it is from Him." Daniel Callahan, after quoting Ramsey, goes on to say that in this formulation, "man must respect his own life and the life of others not only because it is grounded in God, but, equally important because God has given man life as a value to be held in trust and used according to God's will." [7]

When consideration is given to the effects of nuclear warfare, radiation exposure, air pollution, ecology, overpopulation, urbanization, the uses of technology, genetic engineering, etc., no conclusion is valid ultimately apart from ascertaining the will of God in such matters. The basic question is man's right to determine the conditions of human life in the future. Obviously any practice that is harmful to the survival of the human species is to be rejected. Any proposal that promises to be protective to human life may be applied. The formation of regulations regarding fetal life must look well into the applications of such rules to the sanctity of human life and the will of God with respect to such life.

8. Compassion Expresses Divine Purpose

As Jesus was often moved with compassion so must we be tempered in our attitudes toward women with unwanted pregnancies. This does not call for any doctor or counselor to condone extra- or premarital sex behavior. It embodies the spirit of Jesus who extricated the woman taken in adultery from the accusing eyes of common sinners. He did not berate the law that forbids adultery. He did not make light of her sin, but told her gently, "Do not sin again."

R. F. R. Gardner says:
Compassion is not softness leading to the line of least resistance, it is not a way of concession, it is a loving hand in need leading them to a new life. . . . We must do what we can. To abort a pregnancy because it is extramarital may sound compassionate, but if it does nothing about the underlying problem it has no resemblance to true compassion. . . . Real compassion involves taking into consideration the factors that surround the person involved. . . . We must not forget that there is compassion too for the fetus. [8]

We cannot excuse ourselves from making moral judgments

with respect to evil. The Christian must stand for principle even at the risk of being misunderstood by people of the world. The judgment that matters is not what popular opinion dictates but what accurately represents the will of God.

9. Eternal Life Is the Ultimate Purpose

God's ultimate goal for human existence is eternal life. This requires a new birth, an experience with God in which the divine nature is implanted as an additional condition beyond the original divine image. Jesus told Nicodemus "that which is born of the flesh is flesh, and that which is born of the Spirit is spirit." This second birth is the requirement for entrance into the kingdom of God where the divine purposes are fulfilled. But there is no way revealed by which a person can obtain eternal life apart from the process of human being. The potential for eternal life is determined by the possession of physical life. Both are gifts from God.

The question of the status of an aborted fetus with respect to its relation to the eternal kingdom remains unresolved. That its potential for human usefulness is terminated is obvious. It is also understood that God's gift of life is accompanied by God's will to have that life come to term and develop its full potential to possess eternal life.

The various instances in biblical history in which God expressed His intent for the fetus leads to the conclusion that the divine will determines intended roles (at least in some cases, if not all) during prenatal existence. Among the various complex questions that need to be answered before a decision is made to terminate a pregnancy the primary, and no doubt the most neglected, question is "What might be the purpose God has for this life?" Certainly the intent of the Giver deserves full consideration.

Conclusion

The management of human life for the Christian is subject to the will of God. Divine purpose is expressed in principle in divine revelation. The ultimate potential for human beings is the inheritance of eternal life. God's will for the care and protection of human life in the present setting is expressed both in the course of nature and in supernatural intervention.

Whatever the Christian does to intervene and control these forces affecting human life is subject to the ultimate purposes of God. The stewardship of life recognizes it as a gift from God and as a sacred trust shared in concert with all the subjects of His eternal kingdom. The right to terminate human life lies alone in the sovereign will of our loving God.

Questions

1. When God breathed into man the breath of life did He also give him the capacity to pass it on biologically to his children? Is this the same as the "image of God"?
2. How do you feel about this statement by John Mumaw: "A rigid position on abortion does not call for a harsh attitude toward the person or persons involved"?
3. If it is true as Psalm 127:3 (KJ) says: "children are an heritage of the Lord" shall we understand that all conceptions are God-ordained?
4. Do you agree with John Mumaw that: "any practice that is harmful for the survival of the human species is to be rejected" and that: "any proposal that promises to be protective to human life may be applied"?
5. What are the factors which determine whether or not it is God's will for a fetus to come to full term?

Footnotes

1. Harmon L. Smith, *Ethics and the New Medicine* (Abingdon: 1970), p. 27.
2. *Ibid.*, p. 34.
3. Howard S. Hayman, "The Spiritual Dimension of Man's Health in Today's World," Chapter 13 in *Religion and Medicine* (Iowa State University Press: 1967), p. 186.
4. Paul Tournier, *The Whole Person in a Broken World* (Harper & Row: 1964), p. 53.
5. Cezar Heine, MD, *Abortion and the Biblical Message* (Foothills Lutheran Press, Calgary, Canada: 1972, 48 pp.), p. 22.
6. 1 Corinthians 6:19, 20.
7. Daniel Callahan, *Abortion: Law, Choice, and Morality* (Macmillan: 1970), p. 309.
8. R. F. R. Gardner, *Abortion: The Personal Dilemma* (Eerdmans: 1972), p. 13.

Sympathy

Whosoever walks a furlong without sympathy
Walks to his own funeral dressed in his shroud.
Walt Whitman

5. Abortion

BY LEROY WALTERS

A discussion of abortion involves the question of life and death at the earliest stages of human existence. If we look at the history of attitudes toward abortion, or if we look at opinions in our own day, I think we can distinguish three positions on the abortion question: (1) a restrictive position; (2) a liberal position; and (3) a mediating position.

1. Restrictive Position

The restrictive position argues that abortion is not permissible under any circumstances. The proponent of this position says an absolute no to abortion, just as the pacifist says an absolute no to war.

The logic of the restrictive position is really quite simple. It can be expressed in terms of two premises and a conclusion:

Major premise: Human beings do not have the right to destroy innocent human life.

Minor premise: Fetal life is innocent human life from the moment of conception.

Conclusion: Therefore, human beings do not have the right to destroy fetal life.[1]

It is difficult to disagree with the first of the two premises. Civilized society ultimately depends on the assurance that innocent life will be protected and preserved. One of the reasons our moral sense is so outraged by the Nazi final solution is that innocent human life was destroyed on a massive scale.

The second premise in the argument is that fetal life is innocent human life from the moment of conception. There are really two assertions in this premise, that *fetal life is innocent life* and that *fetal life is human life*. It is difficult to see how anyone could ascribe deliberate wrongdoing to a fetus. Developmental psychologists disagree on the exact stage at which a child or young person can make independent moral judgments and thus be held accountable for his actions. None of them, however, has proposed that this stage is reached prenatally. Thus in the moral sense of the term "innocent," fetal life can certainly be called innocent life.

From the fields of reproductive biology and of genetics one can adduce impressive evidence for the second assertion: that fetal life is human life. The clearest line in all of prenatal life seems to be the moment of conception. The probabilities shift enormously at that point. Before conception it is not at all clear which of the approximately 200 million spermatozoa in an ejaculate will fertilize which of the approximately 300 ova produced by the average woman. After the moment of conception, barring human intervention, the chances are four in five that the zygote will develop to maturity and that an infant will be born.[2] Thus the moment of conception represents a much greater shift in probabilities than any other subsequent moment — even the moment of birth.

Genetically speaking, the entire future human being is potentially present in the zygote. A unique genetic code has been set up, and unless twinning occurs, *it is unlikely that that particular code will ever be repeated in human history.* If the single-celled zygote is not interfered with, it will in most cases eventually give rise to a unique and unrepeatable human being. Thus it makes perfectly good sense to assert that fetal life is human life.[3]

In short, there are at least plausible arguments for both premises of the restrictive position and therefore for its conclusion as well. Most persons agree that innocent human life should not be destroyed, and there is substantial evidence to support the view that fetal life is innocent human life. The logical conclusion seems to be that fetal life should never be destroyed.

Perhaps the most difficult case for this restrictive position is the situation in which fetal life poses an immediate physical threat to maternal life. There are two complementary solutions to this difficulty. The first is that very few medical indications are now regarded as critical. In the words of Dr. Louis Hellman: "In the case of medical indications it is possible almost always to give ideal care and avoid the abortion."[4] The second solution is to say that in some situations it is better not to act than to employ an immoral means, even for a seemingly good end. Thus a consistent advocate of the restrictive position would argue that a life-threatening pregnancy could only be terminated by destroying human life, which is by definition an immoral act. In other words, better two deaths from natural causes than one murder.

2. Liberal Position

We turn then to a second possible position on abortion, what I have called the *liberal position*. According to this view, a pregnant woman has an absolute right to determine whether or not she will bear her child. Proponents of this view need not waste any time discussing possible "indications" for abortion. The only factor that counts is the wish of the woman.

Several arguments can be advanced in support of this position. First, it is generally acknowledged that every person should be able to control his or her own reproductive life. The most obvious way to control reproductive life is through contraceptive measures. However, contraception sometimes fails. Therefore abortion should be available as a back-up system, a method for undoing contraceptive failure.[5]

Second, at least during the first several months the conceptus is completely dependent on the woman for nourishment and life. It cannot survive apart from the woman's body. One must therefore conclude that a nonviable embryo or fetus is de facto a part of the woman's body. It follows logically that a woman can ask to have this part of her body removed, just as she could request surgery for a facial mole or an infected appendix.

Third, unwanted children are a threat to society. They have

a statistically higher-than-average rate of psychiatric disturbances, criminal and other antisocial behavior. As adults, they tend to be incompetent parents and to breed yet another generation of unwanted children. Later generations merely repeat this vicious cycle. Therefore we conclude that society has no reason to deny an abortion to any woman who wants one. In fact, the welfare of society will be promoted if pregnant women are given the absolute right to determine whether or not to bear children.[6]

Various techniques might be employed to dramatize the cogency of the foregoing series of arguments. Consider, for example, the following scene from a women's-liberation drama:

> . . . A man wakes up to find (that) a uterus has been implanted in him with a fetus in it. He demands that the woman doctor remove it. She refuses, arguing that human life is involved. He points out that his body wasn't meant to bear children. The doctor retorts that many women's bodies are equally unsuited to childbearing. He says that pregnancy will make it impossible for him to go on with his career, and will shatter the pattern of his life, and she replies that many women feel the same way when they discover they are pregnant.[7]

Perhaps the weakest link in the liberal argument is its assertion that the embryo or fetus is a part of the woman's body. The conceptus certainly resides *in* the body of the female; however, it is not a part of her body in the same sense as her appendix is. Each cell of the woman's appendix carries a complete set of her very own chromosomes. The cells of the fetus, on the other hand, contain chromosomal material both from the woman and from another human being. Thus, genetically speaking, the conceptus is a unique entity, qualitatively different from any other part of the woman's body.

3. Mediating Position

We turn, then, to the third position on abortion, which I have called a *mediating position*. This approach attempts to take account of a plurality of values, rather than according absolute value either to fetal life or to the desire of the woman. It inevitably involves the decision-maker in a complex process of drawing lines or weighing various factors.

In extreme cases this process of weighing and balancing can lead to relatively clear answers. Most of us would argue that if the life of the fetus seriously endangers the physical life of a woman, the mother's life should take precedence over fetal life. On the other hand, we might raise ethical questions if a couple elected to abort a fetus merely because the pregnancy threatened to interfere with a ski-vacation.

These extreme and relatively simple cases should not blind us to the fact that there are truly difficult and tragic cases, in which the relative weight of competing values is virtually impossible to assess. In cases of rape, the woman is innocent, but so is the fetus. If a woman in her forties unexpectedly becomes pregnant, the birth of a late child can seriously undermine both her own mental health and relationships within the family. To cite a third example, using the newly developed technique of amniocentesis, the physician can warn a couple at the fourth month of pregnancy that their child when born will be a mongoloid child. What should he then advise the couple to do?

The obvious weakness of the mediating position is that it does not provide clear, unambiguous answers as the restrictive and liberal positions do. Critics of the mediating position charge that it leads to arbitrary decisions or to a merely situational ethic. Defenders of this third position reply that they affirm certain general ethical principles and moral values but that each particular case must be evaluated in terms of these principles and values.

During the past few years I have frequently asked myself whether the historic peace churches have a unique perspective to offer on the problem of abortion. In particular, I have often wondered whether pacifism on the war question logically leads to the restrictive position on the abortion question.

Among Quakers an anti-war stance does not necessarily seem to be correlated with an anti-abortion position. In a recent report entitled *Who Shall Live? Man's Control over Birth and Death*, a Quaker study group tended toward the liberal position on abortion. The authors accepted a wide variety of possible grounds for abortion and repeatedly emphasized that the fetus is a potential rather than an actual human being.[8]

On the other hand, however, there seems to be a perceptible movement among Mennonites toward a more restrictive position on abortion. About a year ago, John Howard Yoder told me of the experience of an informal study group in the Goshen-Elkhart area. As the group reflected on the abortion question, most members came to believe that the peace position does have implications for one's attitude toward abortion. In a recent issue of the *Mennonite Medical Messenger*, Paul Erb reported that the Noonan book on abortion contributed to a similar change in his viewpoint:

> This book made a timely and needed contribution to my thinking. Without having made any particular study of the subject, I am afraid I was about to assume that abortion is one of those things in modern life that we do not like, but that we are probably going to have to live with. Now I am a convert to a position of deep conviction that this is an issue of morality on which a Christian conscience cannot be tolerant or neutral.[9]

One of the points we may want to ponder is whether the Christian pacifist's respect for human life should extend to concern for the protection of the human fetus.

Questions

1. What is your response to this statement: "The legalizing of abortion is a step toward infanticide and euthanasia"?
2. Contraception avoids the union of sperms and half-cells. Abortion destroys the product of this union. How is this information pertinent to the considerations of population control?
3. What value would there be if the church would take a "stand" on abortion in the same way it has taken a "stand" on war?
4. What kind of law seems the most Christian — restrictive, moderate, or permissive?
5. What would you say to a person who says, "I find it easy to arrive at a position on abortion for myself, but hard to know what my responsibility is to others who are faced with this decision"?

6. Who would best be served by requiring that all facilities offering therapeutic abortion give counsel to the patient?
7. What, if any, are the unique perspectives that the historic peace churches bring to the consideration of abortion?

Footnotes

1. Daniel Callahan, *Abortion: Law, Choice, and Morality* (New York, Macmillan Company, 1970), pp. 418-426.

2. John T. Noonan, Jr., "An Almost Absolute Value in History," in *The Morality of Abortion: Legal and Historical Perspectives,* edited by John T. Noonan, Jr. (Cambridge, Mass.: Harvard University Press, 1970), pp. 53-56.

3. Callahan, *Abortion,* pp. 378-383.

4. *Abortion in the United States,* edited by Mary S. Calderone (New York: Hoeber Division of Harper & Brothers, 1958), p. 95.

5. Cf. Callahan, *Abortion,* pp. 460, 461.

6. *Ibid.,* pp. 77, 454-460.

7. From a short play written by Myrna Lamb and entitled "What Have You Done for Me Lately?" Reported by Rosalyn Regelson, "Is Motherhood Holy? Not Any More," *New York Times,* May 18, 1969, p. D5; cited by Callahan, *Abortion,* p. 482, n. 35.

8. Cadbury, H. J., *et al., Who Shall Live? Man's Control over Birth and Death; A Report Prepared for the American Friends Service Committee* (New York: Hill and Wang, 1970), pp. 14-41.

9. "What About Easier Abortion Laws?" *Mennonite Medical Messenger* (July-September, 1972), p. 18.

6. Abortion: A Personal Dilemma

BY HELEN ALDERFER

There are many facts and figures about abortion such as the estimate that there are 30,000,000 abortions a year in the world. A number like that is so large that it can hardly be comprehended. The imagination is not big enough to grasp the personal dilemma of 30,000,000 women with unwanted pregnancies who did get an abortion. The unknown number who contemplated but did not get an abortion would be another hard to comprehend figure.

It is only when one begins to think of a person at the point of decision as to whether to terminate or complete a pregnancy (and more so if it is a person one knows) that the misery and despair, the tangled thoughts and feelings begin to become real. Then abortion becomes the agonizing decision it is for many.

It is more comfortable to keep the subject in the realm of statistics. To take it from that realm, consider one person's dilemma, brought to me when I was working on the study paper which the council on Faith, Life, and Strategy had commissioned. The names are fictitious, the story is as it happened.

Jane Smith and her husband John started their family during the last year of graduate school and Jane gave birth to their son five weeks before they moved to the town of John's employment. It was his first full-time job in a town about 800 miles from either of their parents. The child who was wanted and loved proved to make more of a change in their lives than they had anticipated. He compounded Jane's adjustment to full-time homemaking, to a new place of living and for

John to his work. Jane felt tired and harried much of the time and had to force herself to attend events, including church services. In any kind of meeting, used to giving full attention, she found herself unable to concentrate.

In the midst of the adjustment when the baby was five months old, Jane found that contraceptive measures had failed and she was pregnant. She was sure that she could not cope with another child at that point in time. She began to consider the possibility of an abortion. She had never thought of it as a form of birth control; but when contraception failed she began to consider it as a poorer but possible method of birth control.

Jane needed someone to help her encounter herself and clarify her values, her goals, and her needs. But she didn't know where to go for any kind of help. Her family and John's were too far away, she had made no close friends, the church had not become a meaningful fellowship. She only knew that with every day time was running out. Unlike many crises that persons face, birth has a definite time table. A marriage in trouble can and has remained unsatisfactory for as many as 25 years before someone took definite steps toward separation or divorce.

John had mixed feelings about Jane's wish to terminate the pregnancy but he was sympathetic to her personal feelings. In his own job insecurity and frustrations with the small demanding first child, he was unable to do much more than acquiesce to Jane's wishes. Perhaps he felt that although the birth of a child affects the father as well as the mother and that ideally big decisions should be shared, he had also learned that still in the last analysis, the culture gives the mother the right and responsibility to decide. This idea may have come from the fact that since only women can be pregnant the question is one which concerns women only and men cannot be expected to understand. (This is only one of the areas in which there is a need for the liberation of men's feelings and direction for their responsibility.)

The Smiths live in a state which was struggling with the legalization of abortion at that time, just months before the Supreme Court decision that legalized abortion for their state. Jane knew that a hospital in the nearest large city was performing abortions quite readily. Later at the abortion hearings of the state the director of that hospital reported that they were performing an average of 400 abortions a month, mostly done at the request of doctors who felt it best for the good mental health of their patients.

Jane did obtain an abortion at that hospital, feeling that it was the reasonable thing to do and that an abortion when done early would not be comparable to taking the life of a "real" person. A day and a night at the hospital under the guise of having had a D and C and she was back home.

Then she began to have doubts. She said later that she saw she had failed to anticipate how far-reaching the consequences of such a decision might be. She began to read everything she could on the subject of abortion. She wondered if they should adopt a child, an older one, perhaps a six-year-old boy; she thought she could manage another child if he were that age. She began the hard process of working through her doubts.

Immersed in his work or unwilling to express his feelings or miraculously at ease with them, John seemed to go on without many questions. I do not know if his is a typical reaction.

Was Jane's reaction typical? Roy U. Shenk of the University of Wisconsin reports that studies in several countries which permit abortions indicate that hurtful psychological effects are not intrinsic effects. Rather they appear to depend on the conviction that abortion is sinful. Unfortunately there is little by way of concrete study on the emotional effects of abortion on the mother or father as to whether they feel abortion is sinful or not.

Many factors enter into a decision about abortion. Jane, who had not thought deeply about her theological view of life and who felt that human life did not begin at conception but further along the line, did not see a problem in a decision for abortion. It was only afterwards that she began to doubt her theological views.

Faced with a decision Jane tried to personally marshal the facts. To her they seemed to indicate an abortion. She honestly did not think that she would be able to take the stress of a second child so close to the first. It may be that thinking through things pretty much by herself she under-estimated her strength. Having no one to encourage her to think otherwise, she went on things as they seemed to her.

I do not know if she thought it was a case of competing rights in which the one with the visible personhood has a stronger claim than the one not visible.

Contrast Jane's dilemma with that of Marlene Kropf[1] who was advised by her doctor to have an abortion because of the chance that she may have had rubella (German measles) during the first weeks of her second pregnancy. Because the Kropfs had known a sense of fellowship in the Portland, Oregon, congregation they thought first of going there for counsel.

They met with the pastor and his wife and one other couple whose first child, born with a spinal defect, had lived only three weeks. Together they tried to consider all possible questions about the Christian's view of abortion:

When does life begin?

Abortions are legal in Oregon so obtaining a therapeutic abortion could be done easily, but is an action moral just because it is legal?

Should one accept the possibility of a handicapped child as God's will and live with the consequences?

Could a handicapped child have a fulfilling life?

What happens to the other children in a family when a brother or sister is handicapped?

The discussion gave no conclusions but it did bring some relief from fears and the promise of support in whatever decision was made.

The visit of parents and of a friend who was visiting in Oregon at the time, added another dimension to the decision. Marilyn identified other strands of thought — books she had read, the respect for life which is part of the Judeo-Christian heritage, the Mennonite heritage with its high value of personhood and reverence for life, and her own maternal feelings.

It all added up to a decision that seemed right for the situation. She wrote, "To destroy that life would have been an act completely contrary to my own nature." Having decided that, she and her husband faced the future with peace, not knowing that the future held a spontaneous abortion.

A somewhat similar illustration came to my attention. A couple in their forties was faced with an unwanted pregnancy. The wife had just returned to full-time nursing toward saving for the college education of their teenage children. Not only were their life plans upset but having read such figures as: one in 25 children born to women after 40 are mongoloid," they feared for the health of the unborn child and for the kind of life the family might have if the child were retarded.

They are part of a supportive church family, and went there for counsel. They chose to complete the pregnancy. The result was a normal child. The adjustment to a baby in a family of near-adults is not easy but it is being accomplished with grace.

The dilemma of the unwed mother includes other factors. She is often quite uneducated in sexual matters. "Society, by operating on the assumption that adolescents should not have sexual relations, effectively bars them from the information they want and need, the contraceptives they should have and the laws which can be protective of interests. The evidence suggesting that the less an adolescent knows about sex the less likely he will 'act out' sexually is not compelling. The evidence seems to point to the fact that a majority of adolescents will engage in premarital sexual relations no matter what adults think they should not do. There is nothing wrong with 'society' suggesting they 'should not,' or suggesting that it is wrong to risk unwanted pregnancy; but it is wrong for society to avoid facing up to the problem."[2] This might be a word to the church, too.

The culture still does not accept children of one-parent families graciously. The girl herself often does not have a strong enough self-image to see herself coping with the stigma or the responsibility of caring for the child while holding a job or continuing school, or dealing with the father, or accepting her own feelings of being cheated. Often alienated from her family and her church she does not know where to go for help.

Every one of the 30,000,000 cases differs.

Even though there has been increased interest in the subject, still little attention has been focused on the dilemma of the woman who must choose for or against abortion when faced with an unwanted pregnancy. She still seldom knows where to go for the kind of help she needs quickly.

What is the direction? Could we begin by making available the best in counseling, the kind that hears the other person out non-judgmentally, that respects the other person's choice even if it differs from what one had hoped, that gives helpful suggestions to available resources in any case.

Logically her physician might be her counselor (and I am sure often is) but practically he may lack both time and/or skill. The woman may need a number of counseling sessions and she always needs them quickly.

She may find it very difficult to find someone who can help her arrive at a decision. An agency that provides information on abortion may not be set up to be helpful if she reveals that she isn't sure she wants an abortion. A strongly anti-abortion agency such as Birthright may be interested in her only if she decides against an abortion.

What she needs is someone to listen carefully and sympathetically as she gives expression to her feelings of fear, anger, guilt, depression — all of them acceptable to be expressed. She needs someone to assure her that she is a member of the human race which has been struggling for thousands of years over the abortion question and is still divided on the answer. She needs someone who can help her explore all of the options and help her get in touch with her real feelings.

She needs to know that there are five alternatives:
1. marriage, and keep the child
2. remain single, and keep the child
3. remain single, place the child for adoption
4. seek a therapeutic abortion
5. suicide

She needs to know that the decision of any one of the alternatives will be very significant.

Hopefully she would be in a church community of such strength and trust that she could turn to it knowing that it would be supportive in every way. In fact, ideally she would not want to make the decision in isolation but would feel that it could be best made by the believing community prayerfully considering directions with her. Lacking that, it would be her hope to know of one person to go to for help, a compassionate person. Dr. Mace describes such a person: "She must not be shocked or offended by sordid stories. She must not be judgmental. She must be comfortable about discussing sexual matters. She must be objective and not have a marked personal bias for or against abortion. She must be capable of keeping confidences. . . ."[3]

Somewhere such counselors are alive. How can their services be made available to those who need them?

Would it be too large a job for the Mennonite Church to locate within driving distance (perhaps 50 miles) of every person in its constituency a person who would be willing to counsel those faced with any problem of a sexual nature? How hard would it be to make such a list of perhaps four to five hundred names and to make it easily available for everyone? Such a person would also be able to make referrals, knowing the services available in his area. The list would need to be kept up-to-date.

Such a list just might be a good way to be helpful in the personal dilemmas people experience.

Questions

1. Do you think that in considering an abortion a father has as many rights as the mother?
2. How shall we respond to the dilemma of the pregnant woman who is mentally retarded and presumably incapable of providing adequate nurture (care) for her offspring?
3. What happens to the mother as a result of any given abortion policy? What is her emotional response in being denied an abortion? in being granted one? What happens to her self-esteem? her interpersonal relations? her social status? her acceptance by others? her conscience?
4. What happens to the father as a result of any given abortion policy? How is his sense of responsibility and moral accountability affected? Is he "paid up in full" if he provides the money for the abortion? What happens to his self-esteem? his interpersonal relationships? his social status? his acceptance by others? his conscience?
5. What happens to our understanding of the meaning of sexual relationships as a result of any given abortion policy?

Is the consequence a heightened or diminished appreciation for responsible and caring intimacy? Does it contribute in any way to the depersonalization of sexual activity?

Footnotes

1. Marlene Y. Kropf, "How I Decided About Abortion," *Christian Living* magazine, November 1972, pp. 10-12.
2. Say It So It Makes Sense, Vol. 1, No. 2; Ed-U Press, Syracuse, N.Y.
3. *Abortion: The Agonizing Decision,* David R. Mace, Nashville: Abingdon Press, 1972, p. 125.

7. Why I'm Against Abortion

BY VERN RATZLAFF

I believe that "abortion" is not only the interruption of an unwanted pregnancy, but that it is a euphemism (tactful word) for willful and deliberate homicide.

Abortion would not be a moral issue if the fetus could be proven to be something other than human life. But since one test of personality, life, is present it can hardly be considered inhuman.

One definition of "death" that has been medically proposed and legally tested is that death is assumed in the absence of cerebral activity.[1] If the opposite can be assumed (i.e., that life is assumed in the presence of cerebral activity), and since EEG patterns can normally be detected from about the eighth week of pregnancy then the "child" or "baby" (some prefer to call it "fetus") passes the test of personality — life.

For some the major burden of the argument about abortion appears to hinge on the question, "When can the fertilized egg, the zygote, in some sense be construed to constitute a person?" If the zygote (normally called an embryo after two weeks, a fetus after eight, and a human being after thirty-six) is not a "human being" until after birth[2] and does not become a "person" until after birth and thus eligible for benefits of federal law, e.g. due process, etc.[3] then obviously abortion is an act which does not deal with a member of *homo sapiens*.

So, it is necessary that for abortion to be seen as an offense against a "person," that that "person" be identified as such before birth.

When does "personhood" begin? Does it consist in an EKG, detectable in the fetus at about twelve weeks? Is it in the

EEG, the pattern detected at about eight weeks? Is it individuation, chromosomal uniqueness, present from the moment of conception? Is it viability and which organism is not at some place on the continuum of dependency? Is it consciousness and how can that be defined? There are legal aspects, moral and theological considerations that are important to the understanding of a position against abortion.

I believe that the zygote's (or that of the embryo or fetus) individuality is genetically determined, that it will mature to the point of birth, unless arrested.

I believe that personhood is represented by potentiality and that the zygote does have potential. I believe that the zygote is a person from the time of conception and that any division into non-person development and person development by virtue of age (eighth, nineteenth, twenty-fourth or any other week) is an arbitrary one.

Legal Aspects

The unborn have at least some legal status in that the born can bring action for damages (or have others do so on their behalf) suffered by negligence or malice before birth, for example; a doctor, a drug company, a taxi driver, etc. Although when it can have only retroactive rights, it is to be questioned whether the government is assuming its responsibility for the weak and defenseless.

Legal precedents are divided on the question. In its declaration on the rights of a child, the United Nations General Assembly stated (November 29, 1959) that "the child by reason of his physical and mental immaturity needs special safeguards and care, including appropriate legal protection, before as well as after birth." In a 2-1 New Jersey federal court decision, however, it was held that "a mother's right transcends that of the embryo";[4] the decision was designed to protect the right to abortion on the grounds of mental health. A different decision was taken in Ontario, where restraining orders against a planned abortion were issued by the Ontario Supreme Court on the grounds that the operation would constitute a "trespass to the person" of the 16-week-old fetus, recognized as a plaintiff in the case.[5]

In some places the qualifying factor for abortion is that the

59

emotional well-being of the mother is threatened. It might be in order to suggest that psychiatry should "help" a patient to handle a problem rather than simply remove it and possibly thereby introduce new problems."[6]

I believe that abortion is a public moral issue and not only the private concern of the woman and her physician. Some will argue that abortion must be legalized in order for an individual to make her own decisions. Such reasoning would indicate that slavery and child labor should be re-institutionalized so that employers could make "free" moral decisions.

Abortion Not a Private Matter

Abortion does not concern only the woman and her doctor. It involves the hospital or clinic staff, the hospital or clinic — usually a public facility, and in Canada the entire country in that it bears the financial costs through its medical plan.

Also the staff of whatever facility is used may be opposed to abortion on moral grounds[7] but still be involved as well as facilities provided in part at least by public funds, some of which will have been contributed by those who oppose abortion on grounds of conscience. And, where bed space is at a premium, abortions place increased pressure on present facilities.

Right to Body

Some feel that abortion is a personal matter in view of the right of the individual to do with her own body as she pleases. This is based on the assumption that the fetus is part of her body, that it is tissue and that she may in fact do with her own body as she pleases. It is true that the fetus draws its sustenance entirely from the mother but it has its own genetic code and it and the mother can contract diseases independently of each other. So it is not a part of the mother's body. Also our society holds that no one has an absolute moral right to do what he/she wants with what is his/her own. For instance a doctor may not amputate a limb or remove an organ without properly defined medical warrant.

Concepts of Value

A decision for abortion is an expression of a preference given to the projected mental well-being of the woman as over against the "importance" given to the carrying of pregnancy to term. Such a choice is a value decision and so a moral decision which at least minimally affects the community.

When abortion is chosen, quality rather than quantity has been preferred. But the two cannot be considered separately. The value assigned to quantity will help determine the quality which results. The society that assigns value to an individual purely on the basis of his being an economic or social asset (limiting quantity thereby) creates a quality of personhood which is measured then in economic units.

Effect on Society

Some feel, and I am one of them, that when quality is preferred over quantity, the next step may well be the legalization of euthanasia. Where there is little respect for life at one stage of its development, what is there to foster respect for other stages? There are, of course, those who favor euthanasia.

Responsibility

Western society has assumed that individuals are to some extent morally and legally accountable for their acts, that the government is the *arbiter* when there is a question, and a guide for community education in responsibility. This idea seems to be bankrupt. On abortion, as in other moral issues, the government follows what the majority (or vocal minority) want, and it will take no part in creating decisions or educating the public as to options.

Solution to Other Problems

Another moral concern is that abortion is being used as a further evasive tactic by our society. Because of social stigma attached to an unwed mother and her child an abortion is recommended. Because an additional child will be an increased financial burden to the mother and to the community the woman in the inner city is encouraged to have an abortion. So abortion is seen as a handy solution for problems that are really social and economic. And the real issues of prejudice and economic distribution are obscured.

Legislating Public Morality

The charge most frequently raised is that "you can't legislate morality." This is sometimes cited by Mennonites, who point out "the difference between what one expects of believers and that which one tries to legislate for all of society."[8] While it is true that morality cannot be legislated, it is also true that the conditions making possible the *exercise* of moral choice can be legislated. Certainly it is not in violation of Anabaptist concepts to see this; Menno Simons petitioned the magistrates regarding the need for legislation to protect property and civil rights of citizens; twentieth-century Anabaptists have involved themselves very strongly at times in attempts to make the government stop waging a particular war. If the confession of the early church is correct, that "Jesus is Lord," that concept of lordship extended for them not only to individual lives but to the very ideological and power structures of society itself.[9] If individuals feel — rightly or wrongly — that abortion is morally wrong (and not only for them but for anyone, just as homicide is considered "wrong" for all of society), then they can do no less than seek to give verbal expression to their beliefs and moral expression through the legislation. For many, opposition to abortion is on the grounds that (a) taking of innocent life is wrong, and (b) abortion involves the taking of innocent life. This means that if it is wrong for one to take innocent life it is equally wrong for another — at least in similar circumstances — to take innocent life; legislation is thus seen as the means by which this concern is embodied.

"Life" from a Teleological Perspective

"Life," especially in the Old Testament, designates the sum total of activities and experiences of individuals and groups in their interrelationships. "Life" designates the individual in *concerto*, in relationship — it is not so much what a person "has" as what he "is" or "does." Life is essentially related — it is not self-contained — and involved are concepts of co-existence, cooperation, mutual dependence. The root of such "life" is found within God, and is seen as something that God Himself gives — He is life itself (cf. Numbers 14:28; 1 Samuel 19:6). Life is, both in its origin and in its manifestation, in

God's hands (Psalm 49:7, 9). It is God's Spirit who sustains man (Job 34:14).

First, then, life does not belong to man as individual — it is defined in the larger context of the community of God's (total) creation (Psalm 104:27, 28); there is a collective responsibility.

Second, life does not belong to man as society — it is defined in reference to its origin, God. Even procreation is a gift given by God (Genesis 1:22, 28); special abilities find their (ultimate) source in God the Spirit's creativity (cf. Ezekiel in 2:2; 3:24; 11:5). Life is given by God, and thus the symbol of life — blood — is to be abstained from (Genesis 9:4). In fact, it is only God's covenant loyalty that is seen as a higher gift than that of life (Psalm 63:3).

Life is thus not an individualistic entity that man has; it is something which he *is* on the basis of what has been *given,* and what is to be seen as part of a process — man is to live for God (Isaiah 38). Life thus never *is* at a point — it is essentially a continual potentiality fulfilling itself; it is an organic process; it is a continuum.

If life involves, then, not only existence but awareness of its Creator, and its nature as a gift, the Christian stands as the one who is to recognize most clearly the nature of life and its implications, for God's creatures. The Christian seeks, then, to draw people's attention to the source of *individual* life and to its correlations to *corporate* life; decisions to *terminate* life dare not be made unilaterally. It is this that necessitates the Christian's concern for preserving the life by which God sustains His creation, a concern heightened where he sees the dimension of life which God in Jesus has brought to bear. Life now becomes a closer correlate of presence with God (i.e., John's usage of "eternal life" refers to the *quality* of life rather than to its *duration* — (John 17:3).

Abortion and War

For the Christian, life is sacred because of its source and potential, not because of its economic or pragmatic determinants. In the sense that war sees people and their lives as manipulable options to gain certain ends, it is similar to abortion. Then it would follow that the same absolute rejection would need to be practiced. Some argue that war involves the destruction of *actual* functioning humans while abortion deals with only *potential* humans, the same analogy would hold then to make it possible (if not preferable) to kill children rather than adults, since children have not the realized potential of their elders.

Abortion and Murder

Since the unborn also participates in life although on a different point of the continuum, then the willful termination of pregnancy involves the taking of a life. And it is taking a life which has not evidenced at least one of the conditions that would justify assault against it, i.e., *mens rea*, the guilty mind. So taking such life is in reality homicide. The sixth commandment, prohibiting the taking of innocent life (*razah*) stands as a continuing judgment on those who take part in arbitrarily selecting the end of the life continuum which will be removed from the protection granted life on other points of the continuum.[10]

What We Need to Do

Create consciousness: The first and most vital step we can take is to make ourselves familiar with the question of abortion and seek to understand fairly the options and the positions represented in the debate. Public education on a wide scale is imperative, and the Christian community needs to set the example. Irrevocable decisions are being made — if they have not already been made; public opinion is being formed — sometimes in a vacuum;[11] if this is a public moral issue, then it must be in the domain of public discussion so that when decisions — public or private — are made they are made on the basis of an informed mind and not in the heat of emotional stress or psychological uncertainty.

Create understanding: Some of the problems of which abortion is but the symptom include a collapse of our moral responsibilities to each other as people, as male and female, a forgetting of our understanding of sexuality. It includes the inability of our society to recognize that its economic system is resulting in social dislocations which make abortion an attractive option to those caught in its nets. It includes our consumer-oriented society which places a high premium on things and a low one on people, where the child is seen as an economic liability and in fact expendable in the interests of the family's standard of living. It includes our prejudices against the child of the unwed mother, which makes that child an unwanted child.[12] It includes our priorities that sign a hockey player for a $3,000,000 contract but feel the cost of caring for fellow human beings too great a charge on the society.

Create response: We need to make ourselves responsive to the needs of the "unwanted" child and the abandoned mother; for too long we have extolled the virtues of our Mennonite homes without consciously sharing them with those desperately in need. We need groups who will spend not only time and money on behalf of the unborn child but on behalf of the neglected and maltreated. We need to be able to relate to the unwanted pregnancy that will still indicate acceptance of the woman without 'condoning' the sexual activity which places her (and the man) outside the biblical understanding of sexual responsibility.

Questions

1. Should the Christian conscience govern non-Christian behavior regarding abortion? If so, how?

2. When we talk about being concerned about "quality" of life, what precisely are we talking about: food? shelter? education? peace? no problem world? no handicaps? etc.

3. If tests show a child will be born with a severe defect, should a pregnancy be terminated to avoid the child's suffering? to avoid the family suffering?

4. What is your response to the statement: "You can't legislate morality"?

5. If life is sacred, what makes it so?

6. What factors are to be considered in determining the proportion of our time and money we spend on ourselves in relation to what we use in behalf of the neglected and mistreated?

Footnotes

1. "What Is Death?" *Winnipeg Free Press,* 19/12/72.
2. According to the Criminal Code of Canada, Section 209.
3. According to the American Constitution Amendments, V and XIV.
4. "Abortion and Privacy," *Time,* 13/3/72.
5. "Plaintiff Not Yet Born," *Time,* 7/2/72. See also "The Rights of Unborn Children," *Winnipeg Free Press,* 18/4/73.
6. "Abortion's Psychological Price," *Christianity Today,* 4/6/71, p. 5.
7. One such instance involves Miss Frances Martin, who refused to assist with abortions in the Hamilton, Ontario, General Hospital, and was consequently demoted from head nurse in the labor-delivery unit to regular-duty nurse in the surgical ward, with a pay cut of more than $100 a month. The Ontario Human Rights Commission ruled that she had NOT been discriminated against because of "her creed, but rather due to her inability to carry out, as an employee, lawful hospital policy" (*Vanguard,* 1/72, p. 6). This neatly begs the question as to what caused the "inability to carry out, etc."
8. D. Friesen, "Moral Issues in the Control of Birth." Newton: General Conference Mennonite Church, 1972, pp. 37, 38.
9. See H. Berkhof, *Christ and the Powers* (trans. J. H. Yoder), Scottdale: Herald Press, 1962; J. H. Yoder, *The Christian Witness to the State,* Newton: Faith and Life Press, 1964, esp. pp. 40-44, 71-73.
10. The point is pushed even further in G. Leach, *The Biocrats.* Baltimore: Penguin, 1972, p. 207. "Perhaps we are going to have to make a chronologically minute, but emotionally vast, shift in the *dating* of our acceptance of a baby into society. Traditionally we do this at birth, as the hidden fetus becomes a visible child. It is from this point that a human being acquires his full human rights. Perhaps this traditional moment is not the most appropriate one. It may be that two or three days' or a week's 'probationary' life should be accepted as a period during which doctors could check for defects and parents could decide whether or not they wanted to keep and rear a damaged baby. Nowadays, if parents wish to kill a defective newborn, there is little they can do about it."
11. R. Neuhaus, "Figures and Fetuses." *Commonweal,* 24/11/72.
12. See footnote No. 7.

8. Abortion — The Least Bad of Bad Options?

BY TED KOONTZ

A discussion of the moral issues involved in abortion decisions for Mennonites would, in my view, look quite different from what I will present here. My purpose now is to look at the issues as they affect the wider society and to do so from a perspective which does not assume Mennonite/Christian values or beliefs. I believe that in addressing issues in the wider society we, as Mennonites, need to rethink our traditional way of doing ethics, which seems to imply that ethics is simply a matter of deducing from absolute principles the solutions to our problems. Such a procedure is not satisfactory if one is seeking to speak to public policy questions or to persons who have made no prior commitment to certain absolute principles. It is with such questions and persons in mind that this paper is written.

Abortion is a complex and troublesome issue involving a wide variety of considerations which, I believe, cannot be simply resolved except by rather arbitrarily excluding some factors and focusing single-mindedly on others. Thinking about the social considerations involved in abortion decisions does not simplify matters, for they do not point unanimously toward one solution.

The "Real" Issue

Much confusion in abortion debates occurs because different people define the "real" issues differently. It seems to me best to recognize that in abortion decisions several terribly significant values are at stake. No definition of the "real" issue which gives weight to only one value such as: "Why force women to bear children they don't want when there are already more people than can be adequately supported" is helpful, for it fails to deal explicitly with what is most crucial — how are competing values to be weighed. The "real" issue, if one wishes to use such terminology, is how to survive at legal and moral policies on abortion which most satisfactorily take account of the different values involved.

I find no way to rule out as totally irrelevant such factors in arriving at abortion decisions as: world population trends, the economic and family situation into which the child will be born and the effect of another child on a family, etc. Any of these, together with others, may be significant under some circumstances. A premature narrowing of the range of relevant considerations is one of the pitfalls which must be avoided.

Causes of Increased Acceptance of Abortion

Abortion is a cause with certain effects but it is at least as important to understand that abortion is itself an effect or result of other more basic causes. I believe we need to examine some of the shifts in values and advances in technology which have, in fact, "caused" a more permissive abortion policy, both legally and morally.

While abortion is related to many factors, only three which have contributed to greater permissiveness regarding abortion will be discussed here.

First, there is an obvious and dramatic shift in the world population picture, a shift which is well known by the public in many countries. Due to technological advances of many sorts, especially in the fields of sanitation and health care, populations have increased rapidly. This shift in population has contributed greatly to the desire to prevent births, whether through contraception or abortion.

Second, a variety of factors, but especially science and technological advances, has affected our values in more subtle ways. Scientific method assumes a rational world which we can understand, control, and manipulate for our own benefit. What is sometimes referred to as "playing God" is fully accepted in many spheres of life. Man has taken control.

This has led to a greatly increased awareness of human freedom. We *change* what we do not like, we do not simply accept things the way they are. Also, advances in medicine have made it necessary to *decide* many things about which decision was not possible in the past, the point of death being the most obvious example.

Another major shift in intellectual ethos has occurred which has important consequences for our subject. The growth of the concepts of individual worth, personal freedom, and human equality has greatly influenced thought in many fields. The new emphasis on freedom and equality, coupled recently with improved technology which makes early abortions at least as safe as carrying a pregnancy to full term, have made it seem natural to many that it is indeed the right of women to control their own bodies.

These shifts in society and value changes should not be evaluated primarily on the basis of their impact on abortion policies. Even though they may contribute to a too-easy acceptance of abortion and are in other ways ambiguous, I find these changes good in general. They represent for the most part, developments of valuable insights and abilities. We should not seek to turn back the clock but rather to rightly use the technology and rightly weigh the values related to abortion.

The Role of Law

In order for a law to be properly enacted, it must, in my view, be based on considerations of the public good. Unless it can be shown that the public good is substantially affected, law should not enter the picture. While laws may in practice support the views of a particular group, their rationale should be the public good.

What is the public good in the matter of abortion? Some argue that it is to prohibit all abortions possible because of the detrimental effect of permissive laws on the "sanctity of human life," a value of great importance to society. Others argue that no significant public good is at stake, and the matter should be left strictly in the hands of pregnant women and their doctors. Some feel that the public good demands the use of abortion, in order to control population, perhaps even the use

69

of involuntary abortion under certain extreme circumstances.[1] My own feeling is that the public good is involved in abortion, and that it is a fit subject for regulation, but not prohibition, by law. Laws should not simply be abolished. The state has a valid interest in matters directly bearing on population, an interest in the well-being of women of childbearing age, and an interest in the values which are at stake. These interests mean, I believe, at least under the present circumstances in the U.S., that the state should, in the main, content itself with regulating the practice of abortion and protecting the consciences of medical personnel not wishing to perform abortions, but not seek to pass judgment on the reasons given for abortions in the early months of pregnancy. The chief reason I believe the state should not prohibit abortion is that regardless of claims that abortion is murder and despite caution about damage to the principle of the sanctity of life, it is not clear that abortion threatens the well-being of society. As Callahan notes when discussing possible harm to the life of the living, ". . . no such harm can either be demonstrated or even — for perhaps we do not need strict demonstration in such cases — be pointed to informally. The crux of the issue here is that the purported substantive harm must be *shown* and not just asserted."[2]

This view of what abortion laws should and should not regulate is closely related to my answers to the questions "When is the state justified in passing laws restricting certain individual liberties?" and "How are the moral views of one segment of society to be weighed against those of another?" My answer to the first question — stated oversimply — is that the state may restrict individual liberties only when the exercise of those liberties infringes on the legally protected rights of others or presents a clear threat to basic principles necessary for society to function adequately. Other categories could perhaps be added on further thought, but the point is that the burden of proof is on the state — it must show why it can legitimately curtail certain liberties rather than require the individual to show why the state should not intervene.

Regarding the relative weight law should give to the moral views of groups within society, majorities have the right to pass laws reflecting their moral views so long as they do not substantially interfere with the basic rights of others. Law should, however, protect the rights of minorities in matters which directly affect their rights. No matter what the view of the majority, for example, blacks should be given the right to vote.

I believe the same is true in the case of abortion; the law should allow women who want abortions to have them. It is their rights which are most directly affected, and these rights should be respected even if a majority would oppose abortion. The right of conscience of medical personnel should also be respected by allowing them to refuse to participate in abortions. But the consciences of others are not so directly affected and must bow to the rights of those whose lives are directly involved.

Some have argued that because the law plays a powerful educational function, abortion should be illegal in order to educate people about the immorality of abortion. While this view has some force, it seems to me that in abortion we are not in danger of losing sight of the moral issue by enacting permissive laws. For many, the moral issues are already lost as a result of some of the shifts in thinking mentioned earlier. Restrictive laws have not prevented this. Nor, according to Callahan, have the permissive laws of Japan made the majority of Japanese unaware of the moral problems. While there is an educational component in law, the fact that laws generally follow shifts in attitudes in society means that laws must be seen largely as effect rather than cause. In a relatively literate society such as ours, many channels are available for raising the moral issue. Perhaps the most effective way for law to help raise the moral issue would be for government to make means available for preventing conception or, failing that, to provide a wide variety of alternatives to abortion for women faced with unwanted pregnancies — alternatives which truly are alternatives. Then people would need to face the moral issues without the excuse of having "no other option."

The future of laws regarding abortion in the U.S. is unclear. More likely we will live with the Supreme Court's decision or, if an amendment is passed, see the restoration of restrictive laws. Regardless of the outcome of the debate on abortion laws, it seems doubtful that what I believe is one of the most important legal tasks will be undertaken — making available real alternatives to abortion. Laws making contraceptives available and which provide various kinds of assistance enabling women to bear and raise children who would have otherwise been aborted are needed whether laws be permissive or restrictive. What are some such laws? How can we promote their adoption? This is one point at which Mennonites should perhaps become involved in state decisions affecting abortion.[3]

Impact on Societal Values

First, permissive abortion laws allow greater individual freedom of choice. Freedom of choice regarding abortion is in danger of fostering the view that one need not live with the results of a decision, that it can always be corrected later. If this freedom regarding abortion is to avoid that pitfall, the seriousness of abortion must be kept in public view. Abortion must be seen as a bad solution to a problem which should have been avoided. People should know that the proper point at which to exercise free choice is before conception, not after. People should be taught to carefully weigh the results of choices so that good choices are more likely made. This, rather than legal coercion, is the answer to the problem of fostering responsible action.

The other danger which I see with respect to the broadening of individual choice to include abortion decisions relates to the fact that our society is very individualistic. Allowing women to make abortion choices runs the risk of exacerbating the unhealthy view that because one has the right to choose, one may just as well choose without consulting others. We tend to feel that our "private" affairs ought not concern anyone else. We are in need of a more holistic view which sees the connections between people. We need a sense of community rather than isolation. By removing societal controls in abortion decisions, we are in danger of fostering excessive individualism because our society seems to know little about any style of decision-making other than edict from on high or completely private choice. Perhaps we Mennonites, with our history of community participation in decision-making, can contribute something to society by pointing to another way of making free choices.

Assessing fully the impact of abortion on the principle of the right to bodily life is impossible. Hard data does not show any impact, but such things are virtually impossible to measure. We may suspect that abortions must erode this principle but do not really know. We must be sensitive to the danger and seek to counter those rationales for abortion which are potentially of greatest danger to the view that every human being has a right to bodily life. The biggest danger to the view that bodily human life is to be respected is, I believe, the view that the value of human life is derived from the work, the judgment, or the feelings of other persons. Either the value of human life must be based on belief in the inherent value of human life or on the belief that God values human life. Such a base would not remove the necessity of deciding when human life is to be ended in the case of persons kept alive by extraordinary means or of deciding when abortions are to be performed. But it would, I believe, help protect the general principle of preserving life and make shifts to other forms of killing more difficult.

Alternatives

I believe that no decision to abort is unambiguously good. Abortions can, at their best, be only the least bad of a number of bad options. On this it seems to me that all concerned people should agree — abortion is not an ideal solution to the problem it "solves." Alternatives to it are needed. They must be created at several levels, only three of which, dealing with the wider society, will be mentioned here. On the level of social mores, unwed mothers must be accepted, putting children up for adoption must be accepted, birth control measures must be accepted, and the view that abortion is a serious matter not to be taken lightly must be kept alive. On the level of government, a willingness to assist women both by providing contraceptive help and by supporting those who raise children they decide to bear instead of abort must be fostered, and information about birth control and alternatives to abortion must be presented in schools. Finally, on the level of medical technology, work must proceed on developing better contraceptive devices. For although the fact that medically safe abortions are now possible is a cause for some cheering, the fact that abortion entails the death of the fetus smothers these cheers with sadness. "The time for loud cheering will come when, through a still more refined technological development, a method of birth control is discovered which does not require that we make a choice between the life of a conceptus and those other human values and goods we count important. It is possible to settle for and become content with bad choices. It is better to seek good ones."[4]

Questions

1. How do you feel about this line of reasoning: "If one has the *right* to choose one might as well do it"?
2. What are the realistic alternatives to abortion?
3. Rank these factors according to their relevance in making a decision about abortion:
   a. The economic and family situation in which the child will be born.
   b. The effect of another child on the family.
   c. The circumstances under which the pregnancy began.
   d. The chance that the child will be retarded.
   e. A strong desire on the part of the mother for an abortion, whatever reasons.
   f. The physical health or even life of the mother.
   g. The obvious fact that the fetus, however valued, will be killed by an abortion.
   h. World population trends.
4. What is the function of law in society? What is the intended function of abortion laws?
5. When is the state justified in passing laws restricting certain individual liberties?
6. How are the moral values of one segment of society to be weighed against those of another?
7. How does enforceability affect laws? abortion laws?

Footnotes

1. See Kingsley Davis, "Population Policy: Will Current Programs Succeed?" and Garrett Hardin, "Multiple Paths to Population Control," in *The American Population Debate*, ed. by Daniel Callahan for example.

2. Callahan, p. 475.

3. Assistance such as I have proposed here would likely have the effect of increasing the birthrate, particularly if abortion laws were restrictive. I believe that at present this problem could be handled in our society primarily by the use of educational programs aimed at promoting small families and free access to contraceptives.

4. Callahan, p. 506.

9. How Abortion Affects Institutions

BY MARVIN H. EWERT

Institutions come into existence for the purpose of meeting needs that people in society perceive they have. The kind of institution and the manner in which it is organized depends upon the particular need or needs which are to be met. And institutions are viable and survive so long as they are responsive to society's perceived needs, and as long as society continues to find acceptable the particular way in which the institution goes about meeting these needs.

An illustration of this is the manner in which the needs of parentless children have been and are currently being met in our society. At one time orphanages were built to meet the needs of these children. Society has come to see that the needs of parentless children can be much better met by foster home placement.

So we might well say that among an institution's prime responsibilities is to be aware and be responsive to the perceived needs of society in which it seeks to exist, and then to provide services which are deemed adequate to meet those needs.

In examining the institution in society, it must also be recognized that in addition to the necessity to be responsive to society and its dependence upon society's sanction, the institution develops a center of its own out of which it can react and, within limits, be independent. Through certain experiences, depth of investigation, expertise that has been developed, and just a different perspective from which issues and questions are viewed, very helpful ways of seeing needs in society and effective means of meeting them often are devised, while other parts of its society are not thus involved.

For purposes of this discussion of institutional responsibilities with reference to abortion, the hospital will be used as a representative institution. But it could as well be applicable to other institutions where abortions will be performed — nursing homes, convalescent hospitals, physician's offices, and other facilities, including freestanding ambulatory surgical units.

Before the relaxing of abortion laws, the ratio of abortions done outside the hospital compared to those which were permitted by law and done in hospitals could easily have been 1,000/1 according to reliable estimates. It is anticipated that more abortions will be done in the hospital in the future, given current attitudes and present legal provisions.

Therefore, the institution's responsibility to society and its perceived needs must be heavily weighed when we begin the job of identifying the institution's responsibilities in something that is as value-laden as the matter of abortion. It must also not be forgotten that in this instance it is a health care institution which has a tradition in which certain values have been developed and accepted.

The Legal Situation

It takes but little reflection to become aware of the fact that a social revolution of considerable proportions has been taking place in our society over the past ten years. Whatever consensus there may once have been about such things as the rightness of monogamy, the wrongness of premarital and extramarital sexual relations, and prohibitions against abortion has today been largely replaced by a pluralism of value systems.

It was against this general situation in society that very restrictive abortion laws in the various states suddenly were being challenged in the courts and the halls of legislatures and were being revised on every hand. Colorado, North Carolina, and California were the first to have new laws, in 1967. Prior to that time, in most states with some variations the laws permitted what is generally referred to as therapeutic abortions. This meant that an abortion could be performed to save the life of the mother. In some instances the law also provided for abortion when a pregnancy was the result of rape or incest.

The liberalized Colorado abortion law adopted in April 1967, broadened the basis for permitting abortion to include serious impairment of the mother's mental health or the likelihood that the child to be born would have grave and permanent physical deformity or mental retardation. In some states, such as Kansas and California, the liberalized abortion laws required that an abortion could be done only after a panel of two or three physicians, excluding the one who was to perform the abortion, agreed that the abortion was justified on the basis of the statutory provisions. Also, in more than one instance the revised laws provided that only licensed physicians could perform abortions, and then only in hospitals accredited by the Joint Commission on Accreditation of Hospitals. This was true of the Kansas law enacted in 1969, and also the California law. The most liberal law became effective in New York on July 1, 1970. It made abortion available on what has become known as demand. All the statute required was for a pregnant woman wishing an abortion to find a physician who was willing to perform it. No public justification was required, nor was it necessary to do it in a licensed or accredited hospital. All that was needed was for a woman to request an abortion and for a licensed physician to agree to do it.

From the end of 1966 until the end of 1971, seventeen states took action to liberalize their abortion laws, often striking down laws which had been on books unchanged for decades. North Carolina's liberalized law enacted in 1967 struck down a statute which had been in force since 1887. Most of the new statutes followed to a great extent the model penal code having to do with abortion which had been drawn up by the American Law Institute in 1959.

In a ruling handed down January 22, 1973, the U.S. Supreme Court swept away any remaining restrictive abortion laws in the 50 states. The decision also affected the revised laws in many of the states that had already liberalized their abortion laws. It is reported that in at least 46 states new or revised laws will be required in view of this historic decision which the high court handed down. The question of abortion laws was brought to the court through appeals on decisions on abortion cases in Texas and Georgia. For our purposes here it is not necessary to discuss the abortion laws in these two states and the matters that were at issue in the two cases. The guidelines for abortion laws which came out of this decision include the following:

1. During the first 90 days of pregnancy the decision to have an abortion will be made by the woman and upon the medical judgment of her physician. Interference, either objection or confirmation, in the making of this decision by copractitioners is prohibited. (This was an issue in the case appealed from Georgia). That the abortion be done in a licensed or accredited institution is not mentioned.

2. During the remainder of a pregnancy after the first 90 days the state may regulate the abortion procedure in ways that are reasonably related to maternal health. This could include licensing and regulating the persons and the facilities involved in performing the procedure.

3. During the last ten weeks of pregnancy, the period during which the fetus is judged to be capable of surviving if born, the state may prohibit abortions except where they may be necessary to preserve the life or health of the mother.

The Supreme Court decision did go on to protect the rights of those institutions and also of those medical personnel who choose not to participate in the performance of abortions. This certainly constitutes reassurance for those who are opposed to the performance of abortions on whatever grounds this might be. It is also reassurance to employees in an institution where the institution's policy permits the performance of abortions but they personally have scruples about participating in such a procedure.

Institutions Respond

How are hospitals and other institutions to respond to society when many of its members regard the performance of an abortion a service which should be available to them if and when they may desire it and come demanding it?

There are those who, without questioning further, would

assume that the will and wishes of society have been expressed in the laws and that the demands of the people for this service should be responded to by providing it without hesitation or questioning.

George E. Schwarz, administrator of the Family Health Care Program at Children's Hospital Medical Center and Harvard Medical School, in a letter to the editor which appeared in *Hospitals, Journal of the American Hospital Association*, in December 1970, said health care should be defined broadly enough to include the provision of abortions and hospital administrators should help to provide this service. He went on to say that to fail to do so would be to debase their justification for existence.

Not everyone, by any means, views the new climate, both social and legal, on providing abortions as a mandate to proceed uncritically. In responding to the Supreme Court's January 22, 1973, decision, Thomas E. Callahan, the assistant director of the Catholic Hospital Association, noted that the position of that association is well known. He said the association would support and assist its membership "in protecting their right to refuse to cooperate in the termination of innocent life." Sister Marie Breitling, administrator of St. Paul Hospital in Dallas, said the Supreme Court ruling would not change her institution's abortion policy.

First of all, as an institution seeks to respond to the abortion question as it is currently posed, it has an obligation to develop and articulate a policy or operating point of view.

An institution should make an assessment of the society in which it finds itself. An analysis should be made of its various constituent groups or its various publics. What are the expectations of the people who look to the institution for service? What input do the members of a hospital medical staff have on this issue, as far as policy making is concerned? What attitudes do the employees have, particularly those who might in some way need to be working with patients if an abortion service is provided? If the institution is sponsored by some particular group, such as a church denomination, what understandings and value judgments does this group have that bear on the issue, and what are its expectations of the institution, particularly if it looks upon the institution and its operation as a means of extending its ministry and fulfilling its mission in the world? Consideration should perhaps also be given to whether or not the institution is the sole source of a particular service, in this case doing abortions, for the society (community) to which it extends its services. What about the rights of these people to have access to abortion services, if the institution and/or its medical staff should decide not to offer them?

As an institution charts its response to the abortion issue, there are several principles which have evolved out of the operation of health care institutions themselves. First of all, it needs to be recognized that a basic and overwhelming objective in health care services is to safeguard and prolong life, and insofar as possible to improve its quality. Only when some other even more overwhelming consideration comes to play in a situation is this set aside. It is interesting how generally we have quite easily and quietly accepted abortion when the pregnancy threatens the life of the mother. Regardless of where we stand on the question of whether a fetus, especially in the early months of development, constitutes human life or not, we have accepted this.

In the operation of institutions we move from the realm of speculation to the realm of action or inaction. We are faced with the question of opening an abdomen in surgery, or doing an abortion. We have also entered a realm where, if we are really responsive to the situation and honest about it, we become most keenly aware of our finitude. We begin to realize that most, if not all, decisions are characterized by ambiguity, and final answers and solutions to questions and problems always seem to elude us. But we do not accept the lack of absolute answers and infinite wisdom as the justification for inaction. *And so, recognizing that we are in an area of proximate judgments, we assess a situation as carefully as possible.* We bring into the open all the pertinent considerations we can. And then, realizing that whatever we might decide to do might not be the ultimate best, we nevertheless proceed. At times the results of proceeding *in this way are not what we had hoped for or the best that might have been.* However, if done in faith, through the grace and redemption of God, they can be used toward building His kingdom on earth.

Another perspective coming out of the institutional setting is that of intervention. This stands over against the viewpoint that might be called biologism, in which it is assumed that rightness, health, and God's will are expressed in the natural biological processes and functions and that these are not to be frustrated or tampered with. Medical services, in large part, are built on the assumption that these natural processes *need to be adjusted,* curbed, or *even* stopped completely.

Roman Catholic views on abortion and contraception tend to follow this "let biology take its course" point of view, and any intervention is looked upon as being wrong.

In dealing with illness and health, health institutions have in recent years again brought into focus the perspective of treating the whole man. The perspective today is to look at an illness or a health problem in terms of the patient's total life experience. Taking this approach, it may at times be more important to treat a religious or a sociological problem to restore health than to treat a physical one. This looking at the total situation and taking a whole person approach when confronted with an unwanted pregnancy or dealing with the abortion issue on a more general level seems to be one that is proper and helpful.

The whole person and person-centered approach should be seen as very important as an institution responds to the abortion issue. It appears that it would be very easy to treat the whole matter on a very impersonal level. On the one hand, abortions can be done in an almost assembly-line fashion, with little or no regard for the persons involved. The one- or two-day hospitalizations, or no hospitalizations at all, and the confidentiality and anonymity that attend even legal abortions all tend to abet impersonality. On the other hand, when institutions and persons do not do abortions, or when requests for abortions are denied, cases likewise need to be handled in such a way that the personhood of the individuals involved is not compromised.

Every situation and experience of human crisis should be viewed as an opportunity to help people grow and become better persons. This pertains, too, when people are in the throes of deciding about having an abortion. Neither the woman having an abortion nor the one who carries through an unwanted pregnancy to the birth of a child should be cut off from whatever support and counsel she may need and accept. Those who have contact with such persons need to respond by making these kinds of resources available as they may be needed and in such fashions as they may be accepted. For the institution which takes a stand against abortions, it may even mean taking initiative to make certain that the proper resources are available in the community for those who carry on with an unwanted pregnancy. This could be in the form of developing foster home care for unwed pregnant women. It could be in the development of other services which might meet the needs of either unwed or married women with unplanned and unwanted pregnancies.

Some Practical Considerations

For the institution which decides not to do abortions, the issue in the main becomes mute. From that point on, activity with regard to this topic will be maintaining one's stand and explaining why one has taken it. It might also include suggesting where those who are not content to take "no" for an answer might go to receive this service. And it is possible that from time to time one may want to assess whether the stand taken earlier is a valid one, especially if there are those in the institution's constituency who request the service.

Those institutions which adopt the policy of doing abortions will need to make some special arrangments for offering this service. Just as with other admissions, the privacy of the patient will need to be protected. Furthermore, it has been found practical from the standpoint of staffing and the pecularities of abortion patients to develop a segregated service. The institution will need to weigh whether or not, just from a practical point of view, it wants to develop such a service. It does require the allocation of space and other resources, and also of personnel who might be in short supply and could be assigned to one of the institution's other services if there were no abortion service.

Institutions cannot operate without financial support, and an abortion service should be expected to pay its own way. Nonprofit hospitals usually give the need to render service primary consideration and payment for the service is secondary. However, even some of these institutions are looking upon voluntary abortions as elective procedures, and are asking for payment in advance. Third-party payers have provided reimbursement in cases of therapeutic abortions in the past. Now there is a growing tendency for third-party payers to pay for the costs of a voluntary abortion under a family health insurance plan. There is pressure to include payment for this service in coverage for single women, and it appears that if this has not already been accomplished, health insurance coverage will soon pay for both voluntary and therapeutic abortions for both single and married women.

The institution which decides to do abortions will need to be ready to answer for this decision and justify it. There are bound to be members of every hospital medical staff who will not do abortions and will not condone the institution's policy of permitting them. It would be a rare exception for a hospital not to have employed nurses and others who would refuse to participate in performing voluntary abortions. And then there are groups such as the "Right to Life" group and others, many of whom are quite aggressive in voicing their opposition to a hospital's policy of doing abortions. The institution which decides to do abortions will need to contend with and answer those who do not agree with its policy.

Questions

1. Does the U. S. Supreme Court's decision to liberalize abortions give persons a right to secure that service in every medical institution?
2. In the light of health insurance plans providing coverage for abortions (both voluntary and therapeutic can hospitals refuse to perform them?
3. Do Christian institutions have a different function from that of public institutions?
4. How might a Christian institution's witness be compromised by providing services which its geographic public demands?

10. Morality at the Boundaries of Life

BY LEROY WALTERS

Two issues in the field of medical ethics to become of increasing concern are: test-tube fertilization and fetal experimentation. The first issue, test-tube fertilization, is located at the initial boundary of life. The second issue, fetal experimentation, is closely related to both the initial and the terminal boundaries of life.

1. Test-Tube Fertilization: The Initial Boundary of Life

On August 30, 1973, United Press International reported on an attempt by two Australian physicians to produce a test-tube baby. The case involved a childless married couple. The 36-year-old wife had had her right ovary and fallopian tube removed when she was 18. An obstruction had blocked her remaining fallopian tube. Thus, it was impossible for her to conceive a child, even though she and her husband very much wanted to have children.

Two Australian physicians, Dr. John Leeton and Dr. Carl Wood, agreed to do what they could to help the couple with this infertility problem. Through a sophisticated surgical technique they removed an ovum, or egg cell, from the wife's remaining ovary. They then placed the ovum in a test tube and fertilized it with sperm from the husband. The fertilized egg, or zygote, was then transferred to a special culture where it began to grow. After 43 hours it had divided into three cells; after 67 hours it had divided into eight cells. At the eight-cell stage the developing embryo was transplanted into the uterus of the woman.

According to the researchers, there were signs five days

after this transplantation that the embryo was continuing to develop. These signs included hormone excretions detected by complicated tests. However, after nine days the embryo "aborted" spontaneously, and the experiment failed. The doctors, undaunted, have promised to continue their efforts to enable sterile couples to have children of their own.

There is a sense in which test-tube fertilization is but another step on the continuum of current medical practice. For example, in some cases where fertility problems exist, physicians employ artificial insemination with the husband's sperm (AIH). If some obstruction in the fallopian tubes makes such artificial insemination impossible, it does not seem like a quantum leap to remove the ovum from the ovary, fertilize the ovum in a test tube, and implant the resulting embryo in the uterus. Thus, viewed from one perspective, test-tube fertilization is just one more weapon in medicine's war on infertility.

Critics of test-tube fertilization, most notably Dr. Leon Kass[1] and Professor Paul Ramsey,[2] have raised several objections to this technique for "making babies." In the first place, they argue, attempts to fertilize human ova in the laboratory constitute unethical experiments on the unborn. The physician-researcher does not, and of course cannot, secure the informed consent of the child who may be produced — even though the experiment may well result in his being born with a gross physical or mental defect.

A second criticism raised by Ramsey and Kass is that test-tube fertilization separates human reproduction from sexual intercourse and thus makes a decisive step toward the manufacture of babies. In their view, even if test-tube fertilization began only as a technique for alleviating infertility problems of individual couples, it would almost inevitably lead to serious abuse in the "future." As Ramsey puts it,

> . . . We shall have to assess (test-tube) fertilization as a long step toward hatcheries, i.e., extracorporeal gestation and the introduction of unlimited genetic change into human germinal material while it is being cultured by the conditioners and predestinators of the future.[3]

Finally, Kass and Ramsey raise a more fundamental question. They ask: Is the inability to have children really a *disease?* Kass concedes that infertility can be and often is a symptom of disease. Both authors note, however, that the primary problem in cases of infertility is the *desire* of the couple to have a child. In their view, a physician's willingness to "doctor the desires" of his patients can only lead in the long run to a fundamental perversion of his therapeutic role.

Thus, test-tube fertilization is one ethical issue at the initial boundary of life. We have seen that, experimentally at least, the issue is already upon us. We have also seen that although there are plausible arguments for employing test-tube fertilization as a method for helping childless couples to have children, there are also serious ethical objections to the use of the technique.

2. Fetal Experimentation: Between the Initial and the Terminal Boundaries of Life

One of the predictable results when abortion laws are liberalized is that the question of experimentation on human fetuses will become a topic for public debate. In 1967 Great Britain reformed its abortion law in a more liberal direction. Three years later the British government found it necessary to appoint a special committee "to consider the ethical, medical, social, and legal implications of using fetuses and fetal material for research."[4] In January of 1973 the United States Supreme Court liberalized the U.S. abortion law. Nine months later the question of fetal experimentation has already become a highly controversial issue at the National Institutes of Health and in the Congress of the United States.

Among the various possible types of fetal experimentation, two have received primary attention: (1) experiments involving the live embryo or fetus *in utero;* and (2) experiments involving the live fetus after it has been detached from the mother. In the first type of experiment pregnant women who intended to have abortions in any case might be asked to take various dosages of a defect-causing drug — for example, thalidomide — so that after the abortion the effects of the drug on the fetuses could be studied. The second type of experiment would usually involve the attempt to keep alive an aborted fetus so that various physiological tests could be performed. For example, a researcher might wish to discover at what rate calcium is deposited in the jaw during fetal development. His technique for gathering this data might well be to inject radioactive calcium into live aborted fetuses and then to trace what percentage of the element eventually reaches the jaws of those fetuses.

The British committee which studied the question of fetal experimentation submitted its final report in May of 1972. This so-called "Peel Committee Report" took a clear position on both types of fetal experimentation described above. The committee's conclusion on experiments involving the fetus *in utero* was:

> In our view it is unethical for a medical practitioner to administer drugs or carry out any procedures on the mother with the deliberate intent of ascertaining the harm that these might do to the fetus. . . .[5]

In its position on experimentation involving already-aborted fetuses the Peel Committee drew a distinction: it prohibited such experimentation on viable fetuses but permitted experiments on pre-viable fetuses, i.e., fetuses less than 20 weeks old or weighing fewer than 300 grams.[6]

Why did the Peel Committee ultimately approve the use of live pre-viable fetuses in biomedical experimentation? The answer emerges rather clearly in one paragraph of the committee's report:

> During our discussions we have been constantly aware of the public concern and of the ethical problems surrounding the use of fetuses, fetal tissues, and fetal material for research. In reaching our conclusions, we have tried to maintain a balance between them and the *contribution to medical science* made by this form of research. In general, we feel that the *contribution to the health and welfare of the entire population* is of such importance that the development of research of this kind should continue subject to adequate and clearly defined safeguards.[7]

In short, good consequences can be expected from such experimentation.

There are, in my view, several ethical questions to which the Peel Committee should have devoted greater attention. First, the committee did not adequately deal with the question of consent for fetal experimentation. Indeed, who can give consent on behalf of an 18-week-old, 280-gram fetus? In the cases of experimentation involving children, parents are frequently allowed to give proxy consent. One assumes that in such cases normal parents will take pains to protect their children from undue danger or serious injury. In the case of the aborted fetus, however, the parent or parents have already decided — that the life of the fetus shall be terminated. Can the parents then be expected to defend the interests of the fetus? If not, should one consider appointing a guardian or public defender for aborted fetuses?

Second, in my opinion, the Peel Committee did not sufficiently consider the kind of precedent which will be set by experimentation on live pre-viable fetuses. One need not explain in detail the metaphysical status of a four-month-old fetus. One need only say that experimentation is being done on a live organism which, biologically speaking, is unquestionably human. The fact that the organism is about to die proves no more than that it is not yet dead. If experimentation on live pre-viable fetuses is allowed, it is at least conceivable that such permission will, by analogy, be extended to other allegedly pre- or sub-human organisms or to other human organisms which are about to die.

Finally, the fundamental problem which fetal experimentation raises is the venerable question of means and ends. It seems quite clear that experimentation on live pre-viable fetuses could provide medical benefits to fetuses as a class and therefore to children as a class. The question remains, however, whether experimentation in the absence of informed consent is an appropriate means to achieve that admittedly constructive end. In the case of human adults, at least, experimentation without consent has been overwhelmingly rejected by society, despite the possible retardation of medical progress which such abstinence entails.

In sum, the issue of fetal experimentation brings us close to both the initial and the terminal boundaries of life. Despite the potential gains in medical knowledge which might result from experiments on live human fetuses, we have seen that there are substantial arguments which can be brought to bear against such experiments.

Questions

1. Do you agree with researchers who feel that test-tube fertilization is just one more weapon in medicine's war on infertility?
2. What are some ethical issues that you see in test-tube fertilization?
3. With liberalized abortion laws the question of fetal experimentation becomes a topic for public debate. How would you answer Leroy Walters' question, "Do you think parents can be expected to defend the interests of the fetus, when as in the case of the aborted fetus the parent or parents have already decided that the life of the fetus should be terminated?" If not, should a guardian or public defender for aborted fetuses be appointed?
4. How does one's attitude on the sacredness of human life affect one's position on the problems at the boundary of life?
5. Are there considerations and insights regarding fetal experimentation and test-tube fertilization which the church has that general society does not have?

Footnotes

1. Leon R. Kass, "Babies by Means of In Vitro Fertilization: Unethical Experiments on the Unborn?" *New England Journal of Medicine*, 285 (21): 1174-79, 18 November 1971.

2. Paul Ramsey, "Shall We 'Reproduce'?" *Journal of the American Medical Association*, 220 (10): 1346-50, 5 June 1972, 220 (11): 1480-1485, 12 June 1972.

3. *Ibid.*, p. 1481.

4. Department of Health and Social Security, Scottish Home and Health Department, Welsh Office, *The Use of Fetuses and Fetal Material for Research: Report of the Advisory Group* (London: Her Majesty's Stationery Office, 1972), p. 1.

5. *Ibid.*, p. 6.

6. *Ibid.*, pp. 6-8.

7. *Ibid.*, p. 5.

11. Euthanasia

BY LEROY WALTERS

When we talk about euthanasia we are immediately confronted with a problem of definition. Whereas the meaning of the term "abortion" is quite clear and precise, the meaning of the word "euthanasia" is shrouded in mystery and confusion. Euthanasia is a bioethical[1] issue; it represents man's effort to control the end of life, just as abortion represents his attempt to control life at its beginning.

First we need to determine what euthanasia is and what it is not. Here are three cases. The question is whether the term "euthanasia" can properly be applied to each case.

Case 1. Mr. A was despondent. A case of crippling arthritis had kept him bedridden for years. After his wife's death he had been transferred to a nursing home, where his life became a mixture of pain, boredom, and loneliness.

When Mr. A suffered a mild heart attack, he was transferred to the local hospital for emergency treatment. During the recovery period in the hospital his depression deepened. One day, during a candid conversation with his physician, Mr. A suddenly asked, "Doctor, can't you please give me something to put a permanent end to my misery?" If the physician were to comply with Mr. A's request and give him a lethal drug or injection, would it be accurate to say that the physician had administered euthanasia to Mr. A?

It seems to me that this is a clear example of what voluntary euthanasia means. The patient was asking that his own death be directly induced. With all due respect to Mr. A's medical and psychological circumstances, it seems fair to say that at that moment of despair he wished to commit suicide. Since he was unable to commit suicide by himself, he requested his physician's assistance.

The idea of voluntary euthanasia as an escape from physical suffering has a long history. It was particularly advocated by the ancient Stoics. The Stoic philosopher Seneca wrote:

> Against all the injuries of life I have the refuge of death. If I can choose between a death of torture and one that is simple and easy, why should I not select the latter? As I choose the ship in which I sail and the house which I shall inhabit, so I will choose the death by which I leave life. In no matter more than in death should we act according to our desire. . . . Why should I endure the agonies of disease . . . when I can emancipate myself from all torments?[2]

More recently, in 1969, a bill to legalize voluntary euthanasia was introduced into the English Parliament. The bill included the following form for a declaration of intent to receive euthanasia:

> If I should at any time suffer from a serious physical illness or impairment reasonably thought in my case to be incurable and expected to cause me severe distress or render me incapable of rational existence, I request the administration of euthanasia at a time or in circumstances to be indicated or specified by me or, if it is apparent that I have become incapable of giving directions, at the discretion of the physician in my case.[3]

Mr. A's request harmonizes exactly with these ancient and modern statements about voluntary euthanasia. This similarity tends to confirm our judgment that in Case 1 we are indeed dealing with the question of euthanasia.

We turn now to Case 2.

> *Case 2.* Mrs. B was terminally ill with bone cancer. Her physician, knowing that there was nothing he could do to cure her disease, resolved to alleviate Mrs. B's pain as much as possible. He decided to use morphine as the pain-killing drug, realizing full well that a morphine overdose could be lethal to his patient.

Before administering the first dose of morphine to Mrs. B, the physician informed her as to the procedure he proposed to employ and the danger it might involve. Mrs. B was in complete agreement with her doctor's plan. What she desired most was relief from her severe pain. To achieve this relief she was willing to take the risk that the pain-killing drug might possibly shorten her life.

At the beginning the physician found that an injection of 10 mg of morphine was sufficient to relieve Mrs. B's discomfort. Gradually, however, Mrs. B's tolerance for the drug increased. Her physician was thus obliged to administer larger and larger doses of morphine to achieve the same pain-killing effect. The dosage level reached 20 mg, then 30 mg, then more. One day the dosage of pain-killing morphine exceeded Mrs. B's tolerance level; she died of a morphine overdose. Would it be accurate to say that Mrs. B desired and received euthanasia?

I would like to argue that this was *not* euthanasia, and that Case 2 should be sharply distinguished in our minds from Case 1. Traditional Christian ethics has often talked about the "principle of double effect." According to this principle, some of our actions have two effects, one of which is direct and intended, the other of which is indirect and unintended.

Case 2 is a perfect illustration of this principle. Both the physician and Mrs. B directly intended to achieve one effect: the relief of Mrs. B's intense pain. There was no other way to achieve this effect then to employ a potentially lethal pain-killing drug. At a certain point, however, this treatment led to an indirect effect, which neither of them intended or desired, namely, Mrs. B's death. In Case 1 Mr. A asked the doctor for immediate death; he asked to be killed. In Case 2 Mrs. B and the physician decided on a course of therapy which in the long run had the undesirable side effect of causing the patient's death.[4]

We turn now to Case 3, another example of man's control over life and death.

Case 3. Mrs. C, a widow, had suffered from rheumatic heart disease for most of her life. At the age of 65 she began experiencing periodic chest pain. At the urging of her family physician she entered the local university hospital for tests.

Within a few days Mrs. C's condition was diagnosed as mitral stenosis, a narrowing of the opening between heart chambers which impeded normal circulation of the blood. The hospital's team of cardiologists recommended immediate open-heart surgery.

Mrs. C asked for a few days to consider the matter. During this interval she discussed what course of action to take with her son, her family physician, and her pastor. Finally, Mrs. C announced her decision to the cardiologists: "Gentlemen," she said, "I have lived a long and fruitful life. My husband is dead, and my children are grown and independent. At this point in my life I prefer not to endure the pain and expense of heart surgery. Instead I would ask you to prescribe medication for my chest pain and to allow me to live out the rest of my days in peace at home."

Nine months after her release from the hospital, Mrs. C, aged 66, suffered cardiac arrest and died. Did Mrs. C bring on her own death by refusing the surgery? Would it be fair to say that she opted for a form of voluntary euthanasia?

One of the problems of modern medicine is precisely that it has been so successful. During the past 50 years numerous forms of life-saving therapy have been developed and refined: complex surgical techniques, respirators, kidney dialysis, and cardiac massage. Quite naturally, physicians often feel *the temptation* to do *everything* which can be done to keep *every* patient alive.

In recent years, however, some medical doctors and ethicists have begun to advocate a more person-centered approach. Paul Ramsey, for example, has argued that our chief responsibility is to *care for* dying persons and not necessarily to extend their lives as long as possible. The *quality* of the dying person's life is more important than the *quantity* of his days.[5]

Viewed from this perspective, Mrs. C's decision is at least understandable. She chose to *omit* a certain possible treatment, believing that this course of action would enhance the quality of her remaining days of life. It seems to me that we can draw a sharp line of distinction between Mrs. C's action and Mr. A's request for immediate and certain death. Mrs. C refused a type of treatment which quite probably would have extended her life; Mr. A. asked his physician to commit a lethal act. In the interest of clarity I suggest that we should apply the term euthanasia only to Mr. A's case, not to Mrs. C's.

This survey of three cases has perhaps helped to clarify the *definition* of euthanasia. There remain, however, serious questions concerning the proper treatment of seriously ill or dying patients. In the paragraphs which follow we will turn our attention to some of these questions.

To many observers, it seems that modern medicine has tended to lose virtually all perspective in its efforts to prolong life. It is in the context of this apparent loss of perspective that I would like to suggest certain ethical guidelines on the issue of life-prolongation.

First, in my view candid physician-patient communication concerning questions of life and death should be actively encouraged. In quiet desperation, some persons have begun carrying "living wills" in their wallets, requesting that in case of terminal illness or mortal injury their lives not be prolonged by extraordinary means. Perhaps in response to such grass-roots sentiment, the American Medical Association's Judicial Council is currently considering a standard form which would be signed by patients wishing to die with dignity. The statement reads in part as follows:

> TO MY FAMILY, MY PHYSICIAN, MY CLERGYMAN, MY LAWYER —
> If the time comes when I can no longer actively take part in decisions for my own future, I wish this statement to stand as the testament of my wishes.
> If there is no reasonable expectation of my recovery from physical or mental and spiritual disability, I, ———————, request that I be allowed to die and not be kept alive by artificial means or heroic measures. I ask also that drugs be mercifully administered to me for terminal suffering even if in relieving pain they hasten the moment of death. I value life and the dignity of life, so that I am not asking that my life be directly taken, but that my dying not be unreasonably prolonged nor the dignity of life be destroyed.[6]

Such written documents represent a first step toward greater physician-patient candor on questions of life and death. One can only hope that similarly forthright oral communication will follow.

Second, as we noted above, there may come a point in the treatment of any patient when efforts to *cure* him should be held in abeyance; at that point one's only obligation becomes to *care for* the dying patient. In this connection, Paul Ramsey suggests that it might be a very healthy development to move the process of dying out of the hospitals — away from the anonymity and technical complexity of the intensive-care unit — and back into the home, into "the midst of family, neighborhood, and friends."[7]

Finally, the use of heroic means for prolonging life raises truly difficult questions of distributive justice. Home-based kidney dialysis currently costs $8,000 per person per year; in-center dialysis costs $30,000 per year. Is it fair to expect society to bear the cost of providing dialysis to all victims of end-stage renal disease? Assuming that society's resources for medical care are finite, would it be more just to invest these funds not in kidney dialysis but in rubella-vaccination programs or rat-control programs for providing ambulatory health care to the poor?

In summary, the question of prolonging life is located at life's terminal boundary. We can all be profoundly grateful for the fact that medicine is so deeply committed to saving and preserving life. On the other hand, however, one can at least raise the question whether the zeal for prolonging life does not at times violate the wishes of patients, serve as a substitute for caring, and lead to serious misallocations of scarce medical resources.

Questions

1. Is death always man's "last enemy"? Might it sometimes be seen as a natural and sometimes welcome stage in human existence?
2. Is the death wish always of a sinful suicidal intent? Might it sometimes rather be a final thankful gesture to God as for instance Elijah's "Now, O Lord, take away my life" (1 Kings 19:4)?
3. Some feel that extreme pain and physical suffering are always evil. But is there a point at which they are unbearable and where death is to be preferred to more suffering?

4. The physician having taken the Hippocratic oath, promising both to relieve suffering and to preserve life, is sometimes caught in a dilemma. When he cannot do both for a patient how will he answer, "What shall guide my decision?"

5. A patient of "sound mind" is under intensive care, being in the advanced stages of cancer. Does that person have the right to dispose of his life? Does he *own* his life? Does he have the right to enlist another person in terminating his own life?

Footnotes

1. The term bioethics means almost the same as the term medical ethics, but the field is somewhat broader than medical ethics since it includes value questions which arise in research biology as well as those that arise in clinical medicine. A bioethicist studies such topics as: abortion, behavior control through surgery or drugs, death and dying, genetic engineering, human experimentation, and organ transplants.

2. Quoted by Roanan Gillon, "Suicide and Voluntary Euthanasia: Historical Perspective," in *Euthanasia and the Right to Death: The Case for Voluntary Euthanasia,* edited by A. B. Downing (London: Peter Owen, 1969), p. 174.

3. "Appendix: Voluntary Euthanasia Bill," in *Euthanasia,* edited by Downing, p. 205.

4. For a brief discussion of this kind of case see Paul Ramsey, *The Patient as Person* (New Haven: Yale University Press, 1970), pp. 129, 158.

5. See especially the chapter entitled "On (Only) Caring for the Dying," in *Patient,* pp. 113-164.

6. *Journal of the American Medical Association,* 225 (10): 1163, 3 September, 1973.

7. Paul Ramsey, "On (Only) Caring for the Dying," in *The Patient as Person: Explorations in Medical Ethics* (New Haven: Yale University Press, 1970), p. 1350.

Judgment Day

Every day is Judgment Day,
Count on no tomorrow.
He who will not, when he may,
Act today, today, today,
Doth but borrow
Sorrow.

— John Oxenham

12. How the Church Responds

BY PAUL ERB

The church is deeply concerned with the ethical standards of its members. This is a part of the Anabaptist tradition of discipleship. We believe it is all important to seek, to find, and to do the will of God. So we cannot approach ethical behavior merely as sociologists or merely as scientists. We approach this whole subject as religionists because we are talking here about ethics. And ethics for us is a religious matter.

The church is responsible, therefore, to give its members as much insight as possible as an aid to personal decision-making. We believe in educating people in ethical thinking. So those who are in the "helping professions" need to help the rest of us as members of the church to find what is right and what is wrong.

The church should witness to the total society concerning the sacredness of life. While we are involved within our own circle and our own context of thought, we are also interested in witnessing to the revealed will of God and how we apply that will in our lives. If life is sacred, it is certainly up to us who are the messengers of God in the world to help make this known.

Respect for life as the handiwork of the Creator is a basic part of the ethical position of any church, not only Mennonite. For God created man. He breathed into him the breath of life. He created him in His own image. And what He has created, the person He has created in man, the ethical person He has created, the person who is capable of making decisions on right and wrong, is responsible for making such decisions.

The church represents a communal moral code. We must be aware of the danger of mere individualism. In a Christian context it must never be said, "Well, I'll do my thing. I'll decide my questions and you decide yours." No, we must decide together. We are a brotherhood. We are a body. We belong together and we must reach conclusions in the light of one another's insights and convictions and leading and understanding.

Issues at the boundaries of life — test-tube fertilization, fetal experimentation, abortion, and the prolongation of life, because they are moral questions, are also religious questions to which the church has a duty to speak. From a strictly humanitarian viewpoint I suppose some could deny that these are moral questions, but a man like Daniel Callahan, author of *Abortion: Law, Choice, and Morality*, who is not particularly religious in his presentation, makes it very, very clear that these are moral issues. From the context of our relationship to God we want to speak to the world as well as to one another concerning what God's will is.

The church recognized the need for study and counsel concerning these very complex problems. Preachers, doctors, social workers, professionals and nonprofessionals in the Mennonite Church are all a vital part of the brotherhood. The whole church body needs to work together at issues which almost threaten to overwhelm us.

Any religious group has the right to implement its own values without interference from any other religious group. So we need not have any hesitancy or any embarrassment in realizing that we represent a minority position. We are a religious group which has its own understandings. We have responsibility to work in the light of those understandings. What does the Bible say to us? What has the church said? What has the church done? What must the church do in the present situation? These are the questions that keep coming to us and we do not need to go primarily to one religious group or another to get our bearings. As in so many questions, I think we Mennonites will find something of our own distinctive way on this question. Callahan says that people who are on the liberal side of the abortion question are Protestants (most of them) and the liberal Jews. On the conservative side are the Catholics (most of them), the Orthodox Jews, and a few Protestants. Maybe we will find ourselves in a category that will not fit either liberal or conservative.

The Church and Its Responsibilities

I want to suggest nine areas in which I believe the church needs to take responsibility:

1. The church is responsible to give brotherhood counsel and guidance in matters of life and human values. It is called upon to present the relevant teachings of the Scriptures based, not just on proof texts, but on the total biblical witness. What does the whole teaching of the Bible say to us that might apply to questions about life and human values? What light can biblical theology give us on these questions? We need to find out.

2. The church is responsible to interpret and apply scriptural principles to current medical and sociological problems. We are facing a new situation. We must speak; not to do so is in effect to say that we do not consider this of importance or as having any relevance to our Christian position. Our world today needs to know what we are saying on the question of abortion as they slowly have been learning what we have to say on the question of war. And there are no easy answers. We cannot say, "If we just get this clear then everything will fall into place." Everything does not fall into place. We have to keep wrestling to find answers in a very complex situation.

3. The church is responsible to give brotherhood support to our professionals. In the meeting on contraception some years ago I remember Ed Mininger said that he would like to feel whatever his best judgment as a practitioner leads him to do in his specialty, his church permits him to do. At that time I put it down as one of the ruling principles that we let a man like Dr. Mininger have a free hand to do what he feels he ought to do. But that made it too easy for us. Saying that it was not our problem said that we did not have to be deeply concerned. Today I believe that on matters such as abortion we dare not leave our professionals alone. They want and need our help and the church too needs their help. And we need the churchmen, too, to keep us from making *ex cathedra*

pronouncements without really understanding what we are saying.

4. The church is responsible to lead its members in understanding the moral issues involved in resisting the erosion of conscience and in coming to Christian positions on questions of human values. We need to encourage and promote the study of moral questions in our congregations and to shun statements that come from just a few. All of the members of the church must wrestle with all problems. We cannot set our people adrift on a sea of conflicting opinions and tell them to set out for shore without help.

5. The church is responsible to give a corporate witness by adopting and making available statements of position on abortion and other questions related to the boundaries of life. Such statements can always be amended later as needed. But it is important to make a statement because there are a lot of people who will not take the time nor have the resources to work through an issue. They should not feel that their church has no position.

6. We must oppose any surrender of discipleship ideals to legislative control or to deteriorating social standards. Some may suggest that we do not need to study abortion, for the Supreme Court has already settled that. Some may say that the new morality tells us what our position is. As a church we do not believe that. The state cannot tell us what our practice should be concerning abortion, nor can a selfish society tell us what to think.

7. The church is responsible to maintain consistency in its stance on war and capital punishment by calling abortion and euthanasia unjustified taking of human life. Abortion is a kind of killing, and so is euthanasia. We are against war and capital punishment; then why should we not be against these new kinds of killing which technology has made possible for us? This might be a special contribution of the Mennonites to our times, to our society, to our Christian world. Just as we have had a voice, an effective voice, on the question of war, so we will have an effective voice on this question, if we can find out how to do it.

8. The church is responsible to stand for the right of conscientious objection to participation in abortion operations.

There are nurses who work in hospitals where abortions are performed and there might be tremendous pressures put upon them to participate. Does it mean that such a nurse will have to leave the employment of that hospital? Could this position, already outlined in a general way by the Supreme Court, get real effective application in conscientious objection to abortion?

9. The church is responsible to promote such positive teaching on the sanctity of life as will build conviction and a bias against abortion and euthanasia. Bias is an ugly word for some people, but I believe that a Christian must develop a bias against taking life. Even though abortion may be called for in certain situations, yet Christians ought to be kept from going too far in it by the strong moral bias they have built within themselves against it. If one really has that, he will not retreat to abortion unless there is just no other way out.

The Church and Opportunities

The church does not only have responsibilities; it also has some great opportunities. I want to suggest nine areas in which these opportunities are offered.

1. The church as a covenant community can provide channels through which the caring spirit of Christ can be ministered. We have not done very well in this kind of service. Maybe if we learn better now to do this we can make a major contribution to making abortion and euthanasia unnecessary. At least for certain persons it will become unnecessary because a loving community has provided them options that they see as viable. In crisis situations they will feel themselves enveloped in an atmosphere of love.

2. The church can learn to show understanding and compassion to those who are bearing a child in difficult circumstances. Up to now we have not done this very well. We have shown disapproval and shock. Someone said, "Sure I'll forgive her. I'll forgive her every time I see her." Really the reason some people are so unloving is because they do not want to approve of sin. Of course not all abortion situations imply previous sin; but I am thinking of those coming from an extramarital relationship. How are we going to disapprove of extramarital sex if we say, "It's all right. You haven't done any-

thing very bad. Forget all about it." We don't want to say that, and so we have an unsolved problem.

3. The church must learn how to deal redemptively with those who have chosen abortion as the solution to their problem. How do we deal redemptively? This we need to find out; we have a lot of homework to do. There are some, feeling that they have good reasons, who have chosen abortion. Then we say, "But you made the wrong choice." Who are we to say? How do we say it? How do we say, "Whatever you did, we respect and love you now"?

4. The church needs to provide viable options to abortion. One is to share necessary expenses or to share our homes with expectant women. Such persons need the loving atmosphere of a home where they are accepted and loved and understood. It would seem to me that there is a great wide world of opportunity here for Mennonite people who have a good healthy home life to share with those who in a crisis need it so badly. We can be a redemptive community when we see these persons as people, not just as problems or victims of sin. When in a survey women in trouble were asked whom they go to or whom they would like to have sit in a group to help them through their problem, they voted for their physicians, but not the church. Not very many Mennonite people felt that in a crisis situation they could get the love and understanding and help they needed from their church.

5. The church must learn how to respect the decisions of professionals within the brotherhood who face the dilemma of life and death in their work. Being under a bond of professional confidence they cannot explain all of their decisions to us. If you hear that one of the doctors in your congregation performed an abortion, give him the benefit of the doubt that he knew what he was doing and that he decided as a Christian he had to do this in that situation. Keep the spirit of brotherhood so close that he himself would be ready and able to bring his problem to a group or church council or the elders or whoever it might be to get their advice or situations he meets in his work.

6. The church has the opportunity to work to decrease the need for crisis measures. It can encourage family planning methods that do not involve the destruction of life. Most of

the church see family planning as a legitimate thing that all Christians could be expected to do.

7. We can see that the young get adequate sexual education so that there is a better understanding of the practices and purposes of sexual roles; often it is the parents who need the sex education as much as the young do. Young people are sometimes driven to abortion by the attitudes and lack of understanding of their parents or other older people. Sexual education is needed on all levels of our church life. Our church schools need to take seriously sex education.

8. The church can encourage better premarital counseling by parents, pastors, and doctors. We should be long past the day when a pastor is satisfied to simply "tie the knot" and give no counseling of any kind. We can have seminars for our ministers and pastors on premarital counseling.

9. The church can make some appeal to lawmakers to provide a framework of legality which will respect the sacredness and meaning of life. I do not think that a prime concern of the church should be to influence the passage of certain laws. We are not in a state church nor do we favor such an approach, so we are not asking the state to enforce principles that are derived for us from that which we hold in a religious context. But there are places and ways for us to give a testimony and it must be clear and consistent.

Questions

1. What kind of teaching and other resources should the church provide for persons now living in the climate of abortion on demand?
2. Why or why not should the church draw up a position paper on abortion?
3. Should specialists be responsible to come up with the right answers on abortion and related problems or should all members of the church be informed and work at developing convictions and right answers?
4. In what ways can the church appeal to lawmakers to provide a framework of legality which will respect the sacredness and meaning of human life?
5. How can your congregation provide options for abortion?

13. What We Are Learning

BY EDWIN and HELEN ALDERFER

Our History

The Mennonite Church's position on abortion until April 26, 1967, was not spelled out. But that does not mean that it was not understood, even though there was little preaching on the subject and less was written. Being a people who hold in high regard the sacredness of life and who are law-abiding citizens in a country where abortion was illegal, abortion was seldom a question of choice for a Mennonite.

It was April 26, 1967, that a legislative law known as the "Abortion Bill" was passed in the state of Colorado. Several months later Luke Birky, secretary for health and welfare of Mennonite Board of Missions, Elkhart, Indiana, wrote an article in the *Gospel Herald*, "When Is Life?" He asked the question, "When, if ever, do our acts go counter to God's will either in early termination of life or in shortening of life?" and said that the Mennonite Board of Missions had enlisted the help of some Bible scholars, physicians, and social workers to help determine what position should be taken on the urgent perplexing problem. The Colorado law and subsequent laws liberalizing abortion in other states has forced the Mennonite Church to an examination of its position.

The church continued to ask for help. Five years later the Faith, Life and Strategy Commission authorized the preparation of a working paper on abortion for study, particularly in small groups. This appeared in the form of an 8-page insert in the *Gospel Herald* in March, 1973.

The hope for the study paper was that it would help to begin or further conversation on the subject, hopefully looking toward consensus. How widely it was used is not certain, since the number reporting its use was small. Certainly no feeling of consensus from the congregations was received. The questions of whether or not enough specific help was given and whether too much was being asked of the congregations have to be asked.

Then in May, 1973, a seminar on the Theology of Life and Human Values was sponsored by the Mennonite Medical Association. In October a second seminar was held with more emphasis on concerns arising out of medical and sociological considerations. Some of the papers from these conferences have been shortened and edited and formed the basis for this elective study.

Where Are We Today?

While editing material for this study a researcher for the "Right to Life" organization called from Washington, D.C., asking for information on the Mennonite Church's position on abortion.

R. What is the Mennonite Church's position on abortion?

A. We have not taken a position.

R. Would you say you are more pro or anti?

A. We have always had a high regard for the value of human life. You know that we are conscientious objectors to war. There is certainly a strong correlation between that and how we would approach the question of abortion.

R. But if the mother's life were in danger, you would give the mother priority, wouldn't you?

A. You, of course, realize that that is hardly a question in this day of modern medical techniques and drugs. There are very few cases where a mother cannot carry a baby to full term.

R. Yes, I know, but if there were such a case?

A. I'm sure someone would need to make a decision. Hopefully the mother could get help in decision-making from the father, a doctor, persons in the church. I doubt that a decision for an abortion in this case would be a case for church discipline.

R. What about cases of rape and incest?

A. I would hope that there would be enough supportive help that the mother could decide for life even though she might not raise the child herself. But we have a long way to go to be the kind of support to each other we should be.

R. What if it could be determined beforehand that the child will be defective?

A. I see the answer the same as for the question on rape and incest.

R. Do you think you will soon have a position?

A. I do not see us taking a position if you mean a hard and fast statement of intent which would be enforced. But we have a position on the side of life and as we study and discuss and teach and write it will come clearer.

(end of conversation)

Certain things are quite clear now.

We are becoming aware that the Supreme Court's decision which makes abortion available on demand, increases the pressures to secure an abortion for all women. For some, the question is, "Now that it is legal, why not seek an abortion?" For some, what is legal, is considered also moral. "The acceptability of legal abortion is reflected in the number of women, estimated to be 800,000, who had legal abortions in 1973. If numbers are an indicator of sentiment, then surely legal abortion has won approval among American women."[1]

A factor increasing the pressure for abortion is that of the air of independence that has been blowing over our society for some years. It is only in recent years, however, that women have been coming to a place in society where they both are able to have and do desire a greater freedom in their own decision-making. The pressures in society seem to be encouraging persons to make decisions mostly on the basis of their own judgment, experience, and interests. More and more decisions are being considered chiefly on the basis of "What is good for me?"

Another aspect of the pressure to consider abortion is that

---

1. *Newsweek*, February 25, 1974.

abortion is now available in one's local community. The cost, therefore, is considerably less than when it was illegal, and when one had to go to other states or to other countries for it. Then, too, the high cost of living in this country and the population explosion are operating to reduce family size to two children. These factors add increasing pressure to married couples to secure an abortion when a pregnancy occurs.

The increasing mobility of our population also adds to the pressures on persons to consider abortion. This mobility means that persons are being uprooted, not only from their parental homes and the communities from which they first established their homes as independent adults or as families. Movement may happen several times for most persons in the span of their lifetimes. In this, there is a tendency to be less deeply rooted in any community and to be less affected by community mores and values. In these circumstances, abortion becomes a more likely option.

In considering most of the factors that are putting pressure upon women and married couples to have an abortion the result seems to be that the need of the mother and of the father as individual persons has a higher priority now than previously, so that the fetus is now seen as a competitor for life and its amenities. When discussed, the fetus tends to be thought of as an "indistinct, out-of-focus blur."

These increasing pressures upon pregnant women to consider abortion have in turn put pressure upon the Mennonite Church. Our health care institutions experience this when a request for an abortion is received and the operating boards and the medical personnel must clarify their position and establish policy.

When families in the church face an unwanted pregnancy or learn that there is a very high probability that a malformed child will be born to them, the church, through that family, faces the pressures of a readily available, low-cost legal abortion.

Church members whose employment is in the field of social services feel the pressures when the people they serve request information or counseling assistance on abortion or their agency directs them to offer such information and/or services.

Our Directions for the Future

1. While we may see no possibility for abortion for reasons other than a threat to the mother's physical life, or to her emotional balance, we will recognize that we cannot legislate morality for society. Having taken such a stance the church will not sit in punitive judgment on those who believe and act differently. It will find "something every day to pity and forgive." It will also give a clear public witness to its views and practices.

2. While we, as Mennonite Christians, will not be able to see our way clear to participate in abortion-on-demand, the Scriptures will continue to show us that we have no direction for abandoning persons who have sought to solve their problems that way.

3. We will become more sensitive toward persons caught in whatever kind of dilemma; we will see ourselves as caring persons.

4. We will see the importance of studying the question of abortion in our churches. Instead of taking the "easy road" of saying that a person should have the right to decide personally, the church will disengage itself from general society and say that it is a matter for a group of believers to discern the Spirit's leading and they will pledge themselves to support the person or persons in need of their care.

5. We will plan sex education for parents and young people. And in such a study we will come to a new appreciation and wonder for the humanness of the unborn whose genetic makeup is determined at conception, a unique makeup never repeated in human history. We will think before we minimize potentiality and stand in awe at the wonder of potentiality.

6. We will become more aware of the need for the examination by us all of all of our life values in terms of our Christian commitment, perspectives, and goals.

1. Class Learning Activities

What follows is an attempt to give some guidelines for persons leading this study in a Sunday school class or small group. A key objective for the session and at least one activity is listed with each chapter and can be utilized in the study. A leader would be encouraged to develop more objectives to meet the needs of his class. Study questions are also available at the end of each chapter.

I. The Source and Nature of Life

1. **An Objective:** Summarize what the Bible teaches about the origin of life and define the biblical concept of life in creation.

Activity: Take the inventory questionnaire on page 114 at beginning of class. This same test can be retaken at the last class session.

2. **An Objective:** Work toward a definition of human life in procreation and the meaning of humanness in Christ.

Activity: Analyze the Church Member Profile on page 116. Discuss the questions at the end of the chapter.

3. **An Objective:** Investigate the rightness or the ethical advisability of a therapeutic abortion from a religious perspective.

Activity: Read the play, "Thou Shalt Not" on page 123.

4. **An Objective:** Understand the high priority God gives to human life.

Activity: Ask someone to tape record an interview with a physician to learn what physical conditions in a pregnant woman warrant the consideration of an abortion.

II. The Issues Facing Us

5. **An Objective:** Determine the logic and implications of the three attitudes toward abortion — restrictive, liberal, and mediating.

Activity: Show the film "Who Shall Live?" (See page 119.)

6. **An Objective:** Empathize with the person for whom

abortion is always a personal dilemma. The question is, "Who can be helpful?"

Activity: Have someone review the book, *The Scarlet Letter* by Nathaniel Hawthorne, paying particular attention to the community's response to the situation.

7. **An Objective:** Isolate the reasons against abortion. What are they?

Activity: Invite someone from an Abortion on Demand or National Organization for Women and someone from a Right to Life chapter to meet with your group to present their positions.

8. **An Objective:** Determine why abortion is viewed as the least bad of a number of bad options.

Activity: Show the film, "Celebration in Fresh Powder." (See page 119.) Plan for a panel discussion on the implications of the population explosion. Panelists might be: a representative from the Planned Parenthood Society, a sociologist or sociology professor, and a social worker.

9. **An Objective:** Understand why the role of institutions in abortion is complex — in the lives of individuals, in the sponsors of the institution, and on those who administer administrations.

Activity: Ask someone to report on local hospital policies on performing of abortions and conscience clauses for medical staff.

10. **An Objective:** Investigate two other issues for those who consider human life sacred: test-tube fertilization and fetal experimentation.

Activity: Invite a gynecologist or physician to speak to the class on the subjects of fetal experimentation and test-tube fertilization or have a class member tape record an interview with a physician.

11. **An Objective:** Define euthanasia and respond to the prolonging of life in the terminally ill elderly and a patient's wishes and rights.

Activity: Ask someone to secure sample cards to be used by donors wishing to make body organs available for transplant. Check the local hospital or county medical society. Also ask for cards instructing medical people to use restraint in methods of life extension, so as not to detract from a dignified death.

III. How We Respond

12. **An Objective:** Determine the church's responsibility with the ethical standards of its members, particularly in regard to abortion and euthanasia.

Activity: Appoint several class members to be prepared to discuss the local church's helpfulness of persons in times of crisis.

13. **An Objective:** Work toward a consensus on each point the editors make in looking at the church's past on abortion, present thinking, and making some observations of the future.

Activity: Retake inventory test. (See page 114.) Write a statement of your group's understanding of these issues.

2. Questionnaire

	Agree	Undecided	Disagree
1. Abortion is a question appropriate for the church to consider.	☐	☐	☐
2. I am generally opposed to any method of birth control involving mechanical devices.	☐	☐	☐
3. I am generally opposed to the use of birth control pills.	☐	☐	☐
4. I am of the opinion that the fertilized egg or very young embryo early becomes endowed with a soul.	☐	☐	☐
5. A doctor who performs an abortion is guilty of murder.	☐	☐	☐
6. I believe a doctor may perform an abortion in cases allowed by law.	☐	☐	☐
7. A husband has the right to compel his wife to remain pregnant, once she has conceived.	☐	☐	☐
8. The following is sufficient reason for abortion:			
threat to the mother's life	☐	☐	☐
threat to the physical health of the mother	☐	☐	☐
rape	☐	☐	☐
incest	☐	☐	☐
fetal deformity	☐	☐	☐
possibility of fetal deformity, e.g. rubella	☐	☐	☐
threat to the well-being of the family	☐	☐	☐
threat to the mother's emotional health	☐	☐	☐
threat of overpopulation	☐	☐	☐
the desire not to have a child	☐	☐	☐

		Agree	Undecided	Disagree
9.	The Bible speaks clearly against abortion.	☐	☐	☐
10.	The church should direct society in its attitudes towards abortion practices.	☐	☐	☐
11.	A woman has the sole right to decide what happens to a growing fetus within her body.	☐	☐	☐
12.	The church should provide more teaching, counseling, and other services regarding attitudes toward sex, family planning, and abortion than it now does.	☐	☐	☐
13.	If an abortion is under consideration the church (minister, elders, other persons) should participate in reaching the final decision.	☐	☐	☐
14.	Since medical devices and drugs are available, attempts should be made to keep an older dying person alive as long as possible.	☐	☐	☐
15.	All hospitals should provide abortions for those who want them.	☐	☐	☐
16.	A Christian nurse should have the choice of whether or not she assists in an abortion procedure.	☐	☐	☐

3. Church Member Profile

A survey of 1202 members of the Mennonite Church gave this data:

Therapeutic abortion (for mother's health)

Always wrong	12
Sometimes wrong	27
Never wrong	33
Uncertain	29
	101

Non-therapeutic induced abortion (at mother's wish, not later than third month)

Always wrong	59
Sometimes wrong	22
Never wrong	3
Uncertain	17
	101

For each of the following circumstances indicated whether or not you think it should be possible for a pregnant woman to obtain a *legal* abortion.

If there is a strong chance of serious defect in the baby.

Yes	43
No	23
Uncertain	34
	100

If the woman's own health is seriously endangered by the pregnancy.

Yes	67
No	10
Uncertain	23
	100

If the family has a very low income and cannot really afford any more children.

Yes	11
No	67
Uncertain	23
	101

If she became pregnant as a result of rape.

Yes	41
No	27
Uncertain	33
	101

If she is not married and does not want to marry the man.

Yes	9
No	71
Uncertain	21
	101

If she does not want the baby.

Yes	7
No	75
Uncertain	18
	100

If an abortion is under consideration, what person or persons should participate in reaching the final decision? (check *one or more* answers)

the woman herself	61
her husband (or the baby's father)	50
her family or parents	15
her physician or psychiatrist	55
her minister and/or church elders	34
the district attorney, lawyer, or legal adviser	3
uncertain	11
no opinion	6
other	6

With modern medical devices and drugs it is sometimes possible to keep a dying person alive for an extra period of time. Do you favor or disfavor the idea of such attempts to prolong life?

favor	19
disfavor	40
uncertain	41
	100

A full report of this study will appear in *Anabaptists: Four Centuries Later* by Leland D. Harder and J. Howard Kauffman to be published in 1975 by Herald Press, Scottdale, Pa. Used by permission.

4. Definitions

1. Abortion — The expulsion of the fetus prematurely; miscarriage.
2. Amniocentesis — Refers to a procedure of taking amniotic fluid for diagnostic study.
3. Chromosomes — Tiny bodies inside cells. They carry the genes, the units of heredity.
4. Conceptus — Refers to a product of conception at any time.
5. Embryo — A young organism in the early stages of development — later the young of mammals is called a fetus.
6. EEG — Electroencephalogram.
7. EKG — Electrocardiogram.
8. Euthanasia — Act or practice of painlessly putting to death persons suffering from incurable and distressing disease.
9. Fetus — The young or embryo of an animal in the womb, especially in the later stages of development (in man from the end of the third month until birth).
10. Genetic Code — Refers to the characteristic pattern of genes, peculiar to an individual and which could be passed on to offspring.
11. Homicide — The killing of one human being by another.
12. Hormone — A specific organic product of the cells of one part transported in the body fluid and producing a specific affect on the activity of cells, remote from its source.
13. Retroactive — Having relation to, or efficacy in a prior time.
14. Viable — Capable of living; born alive and with such form and development of organs as to be normally capable of living.
15. Zygote — A cell formed by the union of two gametes (matured sex cells).
16. Nascent — Undergoing the process of being born.

5. Film Suggestions

"Who Should Survive?"

It happened at Johns Hopkins Hospital. A mongoloid baby is born with an intestinal block that can be cured through an operation. Without the operation the child will die, but the parents will not give their consent to the doctors. They do not want the burden of a retarded child. The surgeon promises the family he will not challenge its decision in the courts. The hospital does not overrule him. And so the infant is put in a side room, is not fed, and in 15 days is dead.

Following the dramatization, a panel of experts in the fields of medicine, law, religion, sociology, and psychology discussed the ethical, legal, and scientific issues involved: Did this helpless infant have to die? Did his parents have the right to condemn him to death because he was born defective? Did the doctors at the hospital have to obey the parents' refusal to permit a single operation? Was there no appeal to higher authority? Who decided who should survive?

26 minutes long, 16 mn sound film
Produced in 1971
Black and white

Order from: Audio Visual Library, Box 347, Newton, KS 67114, Rental: $12.50; also available from David Trahan, 1032 33rd St. N.W., Washington, D.C. 20007; Rental: $15.00.

Celebration in Fresh Powder

A timely and sympathetic exploration of the moral issues connected with abortion. Four high school girls gather at a cozy cabin in the mountains for a weekend of skiing. Around the fire, after a day on the slopes, Ginny stuns her friends by announcing that she is pregnant. For two of them, abortion is the obvious solution. They talk as if she has no other intelligent option. Ginny has just one difficulty following their advice: her own awareness of the life within her. When her boyfriend, Bill, unexpectedly drops in, Ginny feels compelled to tell him. Confused and angry, he blurts out his resentment that she let this happen and that he must now pay for the abortion. Later, with a buddy, Bill sorts out his true feelings, recovers his sense of responsibility and his feeling of love for Ginny. Apologetically, he returns to her and proposes. Ginny must now choose between three options: abort, marry Bill, or have the baby outside of marriage. In a surprise ending, she reveals her decision to her parents.

(While one scene seems to say "beer belongs" it doesn't really add anything to the plot.)

28 minutes long, 16 mm sound film

Produced in 1973

Rental:

    black & white — $11.95 per day

    color — $17.95 per day

Order from:

    Paulist Productions

    P.O. Box 1057

    Pacific Palisades,

      California 90272

6. Books and Magazine Articles

BOOKS

Abortion, The Agonizing Decision, David R. Mace (Abingdon, 1972, 144 pp., $1.95, paper).

Abortion: Law, Choice, and Morality, Daniel Callahan (The Macmillan Co., 1970, $14.95).

Abortion: The Personal Dilemma, R. F. R. Gardner (Eerdmans, 1972).

The Morality of Abortion: Legal and Historical Perspectives, edited by John T. Noonan, Jr. (Harvard University Press, 1970, $8.95).

The Terrible Choice: The Abortion Dilemma (Banton Books, 1968, $.95, paper).

Who Shall Live? Man's Control over Birth and Death, prepared for the American Friends Service Committee (Hill and Wang, 1970, $1.75, paper).

Dilemmas in Faith and the Scientific Manipulation of Life and Death (Council for Health and Welfare Services, United Church of Christ, 1505 Race Street, Philadelphia, PA 19102, Code NO. HM-HW-368-10M, $.50).

Birth Control and the Christian, Christian Medical Society (Tyndale House, 1969, $6.95).

President's Commission Report: "Population and the American Future," Chapter 11, pp. 172-177 (Signet, 1972, $1.50, paper).

Moral Issues in the Control of Birth, Duane Friesen (Faith and Life Press, 1974, $2.20, paper).

Human Medicine "Ethical Perspective on New Medical Issues," James B. Nelson (Augsburg, 1973, $3.95, paper).

ARTICLES

"When Is Life?" Luke Birky, *Gospel Herald,* January 30, 1968.

"What About Easier Abortion Laws?" Book review by Paul Erb, *Christian Living,* July 1972.

"How I Decided About Abortion," Marlene Y. Kropf, *Christian Living,* November 1972.

Papers read at the May seminar on a theology of Life and Human Values with particular reference to abortion, sponsored by Mennonite Medical Association, $1.50, Mennonite

Medical Association, College Avenue, Harrisonburg, Virginia 22801.

Paper and Discussion Reports of October Conference of Life and Human Values sponsored by the Mennonite Medical Association, $2.75. Note: Both reports are available in quantities of ten or more for $3.50 per set.

7. Thou Shalt Not (a play)

SCENE: The summit of Mt. Sinai

TIME: The present. Moses, holding two stone tablets in his hand enters nervously

MOSES: Sorry to bother you again, Sir. But I'm afraid we need another revision in the original copy.

THE LORD: (with a sigh): Another? What now?

MOSES: Well, Sir, it's where You say here, "Thou shalt not kill."

THE LORD: That seems perfectly clear and concise.

MOSES: But it's causing an awful haggle among Your theologians, Sir. The Catholics feel it applies to spermatozoa and ova; the Conservatives, only after the union of the two; the Moderates would reserve it for twenty-week-old embryos and up; and the Liberals feel it takes effect precisely at the moment of birth.

THE LORD (puzzled): But why would anyone want to kill an unborn child?

MOSES: Primarily, Sir, on the chance it might emerge deformed.

THE LORD: In that case, why don't they wait to see whether it does before they kill it?

MOSES: Oh, all theologians oppose killing children after they're born. Except, of course, at a distance of more than 500 yards.

THE LORD: Why 500 yards?

MOSES: In wartime, Sir, it is a terrible thing to kill a child with a rifle bullet and an atrocity to do so with a bayonet. But all recognized theologians agree that it is permissible, if regrettable, to blow them up with high explosives or incinerate them with jellied gasoline, as long as it is dropped from an airplane or fired from an artillery piece — particularly, the Christians feel, if you do so to save them from godless communism.

THE LORD: I suppose it does do that.

MOSES: Of course, once a male child reaches the age of eighteen he must be killed in virtually any fashion on the battlefield except with poison gas. The use of poison gas in war, all theologians agree, is the greatest atrocity.

THE LORD: Then where do they use it?

MOSES: Only in state-operated gas chambers. It is used there, with the approval of theologians, because it is the most humane way to kill people.

THE LORD: But if it's the most humane. . . . Never mind. Is that all?

MOSES: I almost overlooked germ warfare. It is also unconscionable to save people from godless communism by inflicting them with any fatal sickness — except radiation sickness, which causes a lingering and painful death.

THE LORD (shaking His head): Moses, I don't know what to do.

MOSES (briskly): Well, first off, Sir, I'd suggest setting aside a five-mile stretch of the Pasadena Freeway.

THE LORD: Whatever for?

MOSES: You certainly aren't going to get the necessary revisions on one of these stone tablets, Sir. Now, I've got a rough draft here of an effective compromise that should mollify all factions. It begins: "Thou shalt not kill any person between the ages of minus four months (see Appendix) and eighteen years (asterisk) at a distance of less than 500 yards (see Footnote 7a, Chapter Three), with any of the following. . . ."

THE LORD (in measured tones): Never mind, Moses. I have a better idea. Gabriel? Gabriel, come here. And bring your trumpet.

From Ray Fabrizio, Edith Karos, and Ruth Menmiuer, eds., The Rhetoric of No (Holt, Rinehart and Winston, 1970).